GHOST TALES

from the

GHOST TRAIL

GHOST TALES
from the
GHOST TRAIL

C.L. SHORE

Pittsburgh, PA

ISBN 1-58501-023-5

Fiction
©Copyright 2001 C.L. Shore
All rights reserved
First Printing—2001
Library of Congress #99-65237

Request for information should be addressed to:
CeShore Publishing Company
The Sterling Building
440 Friday Road
Pittsburgh, PA 15209
www.ceshore.com

CeShore is an imprint of SterlingHouse Publisher, Inc.
Layout and Cover Design:
Michelle S. Lenkner—SterlingHouse Publisher, Inc.
Illustrations:
Michelle S. Lenkner—SterlingHouse Publisher, Inc.
Jeffrey S. Butler—SterlingHouse Publisher, Inc.
Page Design: Bernadette Kazmarski

Photographers: Frank Vennare—Studio V Productions
Michelle S. Lenkner—SterlingHouse Publisher, Inc.
Jeffrey S. Butler—SterlingHouse Publisher, Inc.
Anonymous Contributors
C.L. Shore

Models:
Denise O'Hare Nardulli
Annick P. Rouzier

Printed in Canada

DEDICATION

To Mom—

It is an honor and privilege being your daughter.

ACKNOWLEDGEMENTS

First, my deep thanks to the crew, Chelley, Tricia, Joe, Megan and Madame Lorraine. Your expertise and professionalism are beyond reproach. It was an honor working with you. To my mom and dad, for the home-cooked meals, the use of your car, and the support and encouragement you gave to all of us. To the Polaskys, for allowing us to camp out on their property. To all those who provided us with ghostly experiences and solid documents: You made our research enjoyable. To all the residents of Twin Rocks and Vintondale: Your hospitality is among the best in the world.

And, finally to all the ghosts on the trail, without whose manifestations this book would not have been possible.

TABLE OF CONTENTS

PREFACE

This book is a travel guide of sorts. It is not a normal one, but instead a paranormal travel guide that documents the various ghosts and other strange phenomena on the Ghost Town Trail. While you may think that ghosts do not exist and that these tales are simply works of fiction, the fact remains that the Ghost Town Trail is real. It is located in the Blacklick Creek Valley of Pennsylvania and extends for over sixteen miles along an abandoned Conrail line. The trail begins in Dilltown, passes through Vintondale to Twin Rocks and ends in Nanty-Glo. Due to the growing popularity of the trail, its expansion is underway as I write. At last count, over seventy-five thousand people visited the trail in just one year to enjoy biking, hiking, running and cross-country skiing. Not all at once, of course.

The trail got its name from two towns that once stood where the trail now passes through. The towns of Wehrum and Bracken were dismantled in the late 1930's, thus becoming "ghost" towns. Although the history of the trail and the towns through which it goes is fascinating, the purpose of this book is to introduce you to the ghosts who reside on the trail, in an attempt to make your visit to the trail more...memorable. If you can't visit the trail in person, you can experience its thrills second-hand. The book also includes bits of historical information, such as how Twin Rocks, my hometown, got its name, which is revealed in the story, "The Legend of the Laurel Highlands."

Most of the historical data in the book is about the people who once lived in the area and, for one reason or another, after their death, decided not to pass over or were unable to do so. You may meet them on the trail or you may not, as Fate decrees. Nevertheless, they are there.

To find out more about the Ghost Town Trail, access the following web site: www.indiana-co-pa-tourism.org/gst.html. If you're interested in learning more about the history of the area, read Denise Dusza Weber's excellent book, *Delano's Domain: A History of Warren Delano's Mining Towns of Vintondale, Wehrum and Claghorn.*

A portion of the profits from the sale of *Ghost Tales from the Ghost Trail* is designated for future improvements to the trail.

INTRODUCTION: THE STORY OF US

How we came to be on the trail hunting for ghosts is a rather long and not very straightforward story. My interest in disembodied spirits and the places they haunt began when I was about twenty-four years old during a family vacation at the Outer Banks, North Carolina. We were playing a friendly game of whiffleball on the beach and I came up to bat. The pitcher, my husband, who loves me dearly, threw a ball that a blind man could hit. I blasted the ball into the surf and took off running. As I rounded second base, my brother shoved me slightly in an effort to slow me down and give my cousin Dennis time to retrieve the ball. He slowed me down, sure enough. I lost my balance and hit my head on my sister's knee as she ran up to tag me from third base.

At that moment I came to understand the meaning of the expression "seeing stars." An entire galaxy spun about my head. That was when I saw my family staring down at me. My grandfather was smiling, my grandmothers were waving, and my dog Chase was licking my chin. It was a lovely sight. The only catch was that they had all been dead for years. Ever since then, I had sporadic encounters with the world of spirits. Eventually, I earned my doctorate in "ghostology" and have been ghost-busting ever since.

When sightings of spectral beings on the Ghost Town Trail began to occur in significant numbers, I had no choice but to rise to the occasion and document the incidents in printed form. However, there were so many ghosts that they required more than one book. This, then, is the first of three volumes based on our three-week investigation. Volume One documents ghosts inhabiting the stretch of trail from Twin Rocks to Vintondale; Volume Two, Twin Rocks to Nanty-Glo; Volume Three, Vintondale to Dilltown.

None of these books would have been possible without the skilled assistance of my "ghost crew", who accompanied me throughout the investigation. The story behind Chelley, the photographer on the team, is a bit different from mine. Chelley grew up in a house listed in the National Registry of Really Haunted Homes in America (NRRHHA). The spirit that roams her family's house manifested itself to Chelley in two ways: in a spontaneous drawing, more commonly called automatic drawing, and in a photograph she had taken. Since those two occurrences, Chelley has been called upon to draw what she sensed and photograph what others have seen. While she cannot actually see ghosts, she gets clear impressions of them, which enable her to render them visible through art.

Chelley agreed to join us for two reasons. One was because of my reputation for tracking ghosts, or so she says, and the other was because she had never been camping.

Tricia became a part of the crew because she had a penchant for attracting ghosts the way a lightning rod attracts lightning. If a ghost is within a five-mile radius, Tricia is going to encounter it in some strange way. I first heard about Tricia's talents from a colleague, Dr. Dieter Hauptmann, a professor of Paranormal Physics at Tottenburg University in Klasse, Germany.

Dr. Hauptmann wrote me a letter relating the following experience. He was walking his black poodle one afternoon when a young American woman greeted him with these words: "There's a man behind you who wants your attention. I think it's your brother."

The young woman was Tricia, who was hiking through Germany before starting her senior year of college. Dr. Hauptmann's only brother, Christian, could not have been present that afternoon because he was living in France at the time. Dr. Hauptmann, fearing a disaster, rushed home and called Christian, only to find out that his brother was deathly ill. Fortunately, Dr. Hauptmann had the opportunity to speak with Christian very briefly over the phone before the dying man slipped into a coma and passed away.

Impressed with Tricia's sighting, Dr. Hauptmann tracked her down and tested her for psychic abilities. He described the findings as "remarkable, off the charts in terms of psychic imaging." The good doctor was right on the mark, as I found out soon after I hired Tricia, right out of college. She has been working with me for the past three years.

Joe is our equipment man. He handles our movie camera and also knows how to operate the infrared equipment and interpret the results. This tall, lean fellow with thick black hair and a full mustache attracts a lot of local ladies. Joe has also had many of his own personal experiences with ghosts and other phenomena, enough to easily fill another book.

Joe's ghost-busting career began when he and his father, the former owner of Infrared Heat Loss Scanning Services, Incorporated, were hired by the Rose, Ross and Skinner Manufacturing Company to measure the amount of heat loss from the roof of their paper processing plant.

Joe was running the equipment when his father suffered a heart attack on the roof, only a few yards from his son. Joe dropped the infrared device and ran to his father, who was already gone. A few weeks after the funeral, Joe was running a read-out of the Rose, Ross and Skinner job when he detected a sudden rise in temperature about seven feet above the surface of the roof. The concentrated heat was located directly above the exact spot of his father's death at the exact time of his demise. The heat stayed consistent for five minutes, then decreased and finally vanished as it apparently rose out of the range of the equipment.

Joe believes this heat rise was his father's spirit caught in the act of leaving the body, and it was this moving experience that sparked his interest in the otherworld. Joe and I have worked together on many projects, including the Desert Ghosts, Ghosts of the Midwest and the French Ghosts.

Megan is a ghostwriter, of sorts. I met Megan many years ago when she was editing my first book. Since that time she has shaped and crafted my work (picked on me and cut my best words) and continues to do so with high hopes of transforming me into the writer that she feels I can some day become.

Megan also has a few ghosts in her past. Just a year ago, Megan saw one sitting on the back steps of her house, a sad, lonely spirit with a perpetually downcast face. This was Ralph, an impoverished man whom Megan had treated with kindness, providing him with an occasional hot meal as well as winter clothing. Homeless for most of his life, Ralph was homeless in death and had gravitated to Megan's house simply because he had nowhere else to go. It took a while for Megan to persuade him to pass on by passing over to the other side. Fortunately, patience is a job requirement for editors.

Madame Lorraine, a well-known and respected medium from Johnstown, Pennsylvania, was an unplanned but very welcome addition to our investigation. Her valuable insights into the hauntings are given at the end of each tale. Since she came on the scene after our investigation was well under way, her comments on some of the stories are based on her professional opinions rather than her personal experiences.

It is the sincere wish of the crew that you enjoy your visit to the Ghost Town Trail. Don't let a few ghosts scare you away. Almost all of them are harmless. A few are playful. Most you'll never see. But remember, when you are on the trail, you are entering their home, so keep the trail free of litter, respect the other travelers (both human and otherwise), and obey the rules.

HAPPY TRAILS

A PRAYER
FOR THE READER

"From ghoulies and ghosties
and lang-leggit beasties

And things that go bump in the night

May the good Lord deliver us."

—An old Scottish blessing

WRECKED!

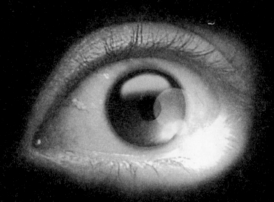

WRECKED!

NAME: *704 Westbound and 501 Eastbound*
LOCATION: *Near the Polasky farm*
MANIFESTATION: *The trains are never seen, only felt and heard.*

What would this collection of tales be without a ghost train on a ghost trail that used to be a railroad track whose trains passed through two ghost towns? Not much, I would suspect. Fortunately, the Ghost Town Trail has such a train. In fact, it has two.

I found this out the evening before my first full day on the trail. I was just a few yards from the camp we had just set up, gathering wood for a campfire, when I heard someone behind me ask, "You guys the ghost people?"

"Yes." I turned around to behold a rather large woman wearing her hot pink T-shirt inside out and backwards. She introduced herself as Zelda Abernathy, a dead giveaway as to why her world might be slightly reversed. I set my armful of branches and twigs on the ground. Her words seemed a little hostile to me, but I assumed she was just being direct. In the days to come, I'd learn that, as far as Twin Rocks citizens were concerned, "ghost people" was the kindest term they used to describe us. "Can I help you?"

"No, but I can help you." She eyed our motley group of tents. "If I were you, I'd move about half a mile down the trail and set up there." I explained that we had permission to camp at our present site. "Oh, this has nothing to do with permission," she said, shaking her head wisely. "Has to do with getting a good night's sleep."

"Excuse me?" I had no idea what this woman meant.

"The trains. They're gonna wake you up, sure as shootin'. Or sure as hootin', in this case," she said, laughing at her cleverness.

I smiled. It was the smile I used when dealing with irrational people. It is a soft, warm, non-threatening expression, calculated not excite those whose grip on sanity is less than secure. "M'am, the last train passed through here about 50 years ago."

"That's what you think. No one told you about the trains?"

"Not a word."

Zelda sighed. "I guess folks are so used to 'em around here they don't pay 'em much mind anymore. But still, you should move."

"What will the trains do to us if we stay? Run us over?"

"Honey, these trains aren't real...." She lowered her voice and gave me a soft, warm, non-threatening smile. "They're ghosts. You being a ghost person and all, this should be right up your alley."

"Zelda, please do me a favor. Start at the beginning and tell me about the trains. What will happen if we stay here?"

"Okay," she said, "it's like this. You're gonna feel a rumbling vibration, followed by a train whistle that sounds kinda like this." She pursed her lips, then cupped her hands around her mouth and produced a fair imitation of the sound of a distant train whistle. "Then you're gonna hear the screech of metal against metal as the 704 Westbound tries to stop. And eventually it does stop, but only after crashing into the 501 Eastbound." Zelda held her hands over her ears to dramatize her explanation. "Happened in '45. Some kids switched the tracks," she added casually. "Now, every night, right at 12:03...CRASH!" She slapped her hands together for emphasis. "Now you might hear a train whistle during the day. Sometimes you hear just the crash. But the whole shebang happens only at 12:03."

I didn't know what to say. I hadn't expected visits by haunted locomotives. There was no way I wanted to pack up camp in the dark and move to places unknown and unauthorized.

Zelda cocked her head and studied our campsite more carefully. "Whattsa matter with that?" she said, pointing to the tent that Chelley had finished setting up minutes earlier. I took a good look at it. Chelly, an inexperienced camper, had borrowed an old GI tent from her uncle. Not only did it sway on its moorings like a newborn foal, its seams were as fuzzy as a foal's mane. Like Zelda's shirt, the tent was inside out.

"Must be the latest style," I replied.

Zelda wandered off a short time later. She had delivered her message, and we, to our regret, didn't act on it. To make a long story short, neither my crew nor I got a peaceful night's sleep once during our entire trip. Every single night just past midnight, exactly as Zelda had predicted, an invisible train rumbled past our tents, blowing air over us and sounding its whistle. The first time we heard it, we all ran out of our tents shouting. After that, we just endured the nightly visitation. I found it rather soothing, in a way. Right up until the CRASH!

THE FLAMING
CHILD

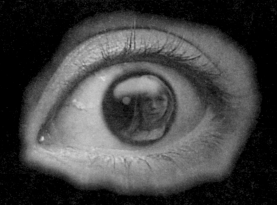

THE FLAMING CHILD

NAME: *Magdelena Bronski-Stark ("Maggie")*

LOCATION: *Various locations along the entire length of the trail.*

MANIFESTATION: *All her manifestations are visual; an auditory manifestation has never been reported. Sighted very often. Most reports are of a small blonde girl approximately six years old, standing alone on the trail or in a nearby woods or field. Others have reported seeing the same girl on fire or trailing clouds of smoke as she runs in terror. Maggie also manifests as a ball of fire.*

A young girl known around Twin Rocks simply as Maggie is the first ghost we investigated. The reason we chose her is twofold. First of all, Maggie is the resident ghost of Twin Rocks; there's hardly anyone in the area who hasn't seen her at least once. Second, I've had two encounters with her myself.

The first time I saw Maggie I was picking blackberries in what the locals call "the strippings," a dirt road connecting Twins Rocks and Cardiff, a nearby village. To get from the strippings to the main road, I had to pass St. Charles Cemetery. While I enjoyed berry picking because it gave me time alone to daydream, I dreaded walking past those tall iron gates that separated the living from the dead. The thought of all those people, dead and forgotten, frightened me with visions of my own mortality.

Around twilight, when I finished filling my pail and had mustered up enough courage, I headed toward the cemetery. I don't know what makes people stare at things that frighten them, but as I passed those gates I couldn't help myself: I looked past the gate straight at the head-stones scattered across the hillside. Then I noticed some-thing odd. A little girl, beautiful in a quiet, almost angelic way, stood just outside the wrought-iron gates. She was as slight as a fawn, maybe five or six years old, and her honey-colored hair brushed the top of her shoulders. She had the bluest eyes, as blue as lupine flowers. At first, I thought she was a neighborhood kid playing near the cemetery, but then I saw that she couldn't be a kid at all: I could see straight through her. I dropped my day's work on the ground and ran home. I never went berry picking alone after that.

The next time I saw this apparition was at my Uncle Frank's burial. My whole family was wiping tears from their eyes as a few veterans of long-ago wars, all in their seventies, honored my dear, beloved uncle with a military funeral. One particularly fragile gen-tleman struggled to blow out "Taps" on his bugle, but managed only a series of squeaks that barely passed for music. Still, the thought was there. I looked up from the casket and stared off into the nearby woods. Except for the sounds of the bugle and the occasional sniffle, the air was strangely silent.

Then I saw her, a vaguely familiar child standing on the outskirts of the cemetery. "Who is that little girl over there?" I asked, my cousin Joanne, who was standing next to me.

"What girl?" she asked, wiping her nose with a tissue.

"There." I pointed. "Right there."

"I don't see anybody," she said, returning to her grieving. Then, in a sarcastic whisper, she added, "Maybe you're seeing Maggie."

The ghost Maggie? No way! It couldn't be. But it was, the very same phantom I had seen years earlier. As I stared at her, she began to glow with a flickering orange light, and I could make out red and yellow flames lapping at her head and feet. Then, like a watercolor painting dropped in a pond, Maggie faded from sight.

The crew members and I encountered Maggie briefly on the very first day of our expedition. We were about two miles from Vintondale. It was near the end of the day and we were hiking back to the campsite. We were debating which one of us would prove to be the best campfire cook. There was no doubt in my mind that it would not be me, and I knew from experience that Joe could barely distinguish between a fork and a spoon, so my vote was for Chelley. Everyone else voted for themselves.

I reminded Joe about the cooking disaster we barely averted when he tried making a grilled cheese sandwich with crusty French bread and Camembert cheese over an open flame. He nearly scorched the entire French countryside. He simply replied that he had improved since that international incident and refused to change his vote.

As we neared a sharp bend in the trail, Joe tugged on my sleeve. "Look," he whispered, holding up the hand-held meter of his infrared measuring equipment. The needle indicated a high level of paranormal activity.

I motioned to Chelley to get her camera ready. At the same time, I rounded the bend and carefully scanned the trail all around me.

"There!" Tricia pointed to a grassy area about twenty yards away.

I didn't see her at first, her image was so faint. She looked like a figure viewed through a camera lens, wavering in and out of focus. Then her image solidified.

"Maggie." I wasn't sure whether I was speaking the word or mouthing it.

Before me stood a little girl, the same little girl I had seen at the strippings and at my uncle's funeral. She gazed back at me with sad, lapis-blue eyes, her face a page on which her silent suffering was plainly written. She appeared to be speaking, but the only sounds I heard were the lazy stirring of branches in the wind and the click of Chelley's shutter, snapping like a rabid dog.

Maggie looked to be on the verge of tears. Then, without warning, she broke into a run toward us as black smoke began to rise from her back. The next thing I knew she was barreling straight toward me. Acting on instinct alone, I crouched low, shielding my face with my hands. I felt a cold sensation pass through me, followed by a moment of intense heat. Then Maggie was gone.

"Did you get pictures?" I squawked, when I regained the powers of speech.

Chelley didn't answer. She was still shooting away, although her camera had long since run out of film.

Joe stood like a statue in the center of the trail, his chin nearly resting on his neck.

Tricia was turning slow circles at the edge of the path, trying in vain to relocate the little phantom. Her one-word comment summed up the whole experience for all of us: "Wow!"

Maggie's story is as heartbreaking as her appearance. According to contemporary newspaper articles, she had been born in 1922, the only child of Paul Bronski-Stark and his beautiful wife, Elaine. Both doted on little Maggie, and perhaps with good reason, since the four sons born earlier to the couple had all died in infancy. Maggie was said to possess an unearthly beauty and had a disposition so sweet and disarming that complete strangers would stop Elaine on the street to tell her how fortunate she was to have such an angel for a daughter.

A letter from Elaine's father to his aging aunt describes in some length how much Paul and Elaine lovingly indulged Maggie. Paul had inherited great wealth from his father, a famous industrialist, and was able to provide his family with regular trips to Europe, outfits in the latest fashion, and other extravagant gifts. Despite all this bounty, Maggie's favorite possession was a child-size gold ring, set with a tiny rhinestone, which her father had given her for her fourth birthday.

Elaine's greatest concern was for the child's safety. This vigilance was natural, her father explained in his letter, considering the fate of her other children. Elaine kept an eagle eye on her daughter and worried to the point of becoming sick to the stomach if she were away from the girl for more than a few hours at a time. From all accounts, Elaine was a devoted mother, and Maggie's life was as rich and happy as that of a princess in a fairy tale.

Shortly after Maggie's sixth birthday, the fairy tale became a tragedy.

Elaine frequently gave elegant dinners for Paul's many wealthy friends, and the centerpiece of her banquet table was an exquisite silver candelabra that held six tall, white candles. The flickering candlelight entranced Maggie, who never tired of standing at the table to watch the dancing flames. Elaine had instructed little Maggie on a dozen occasions to keep away from the lit candles, that their beautiful flames were deadly dangerous, but she was never certain if the child understood her.

On Paul's birthday that year, Elaine held an especially festive dinner party that went on for hours. Maggie had crept down the stairs to watch the diners, but had been tenderly returned to her bed by Elaine herself. While an army of servants cleared away the dishes, the guests amused themselves with dancing, card games, and serious political discussions. By the time Paul and Elaine went to bed that night, both were exhausted.

Not long after falling asleep, Elaine was awakened by a loud thump coming from the first floor. Thinking that one of the servants might be trying to pilfer the silverware, Elaine woke the housekeeper. She decided not to wake her husband, who was so exhausted he had slept through the noise. The two women made their way downstairs, through the parlor and ballroom into the vast dining room, where the candelabra lay on the floor along with the fragments of several candles. Suddenly, to her horror, Elaine beheld her beloved daughter, sitting in the middle of the huge mahogany dining table, a white wax taper in one hand and a lit match in the other. "Look, Mama, I found the matches," the child announced in an excited voice. "I can light the candles myself."

Elaine shrieked in alarm and ran toward Maggie to seize the match from her. The child, surprised by her mother's sudden movement, dropped the match on her nightgown. Instantly she was engulfed in a ball of yellow flames. Forcing herself to stay calm, Elaine tried to wrap the linen tablecloth around Maggie to smother the fire, but the terrified child struggled out of her grip, leaped from the table and staggered away in the direction of the sunroom. Burning bits of clothing fell to the floor as she stumbled into chairs and other furniture. Elaine trailed the fiery child into the sunroom and through the French doors, which a careless servant had left unlocked. She followed Maggie's blazing path through the garden and into the woods, where she finally lost track of her in a thick tangle of trees and shrubbery.

By this time Paul had awoken and learned what had happened from the housekeeper. He dispatched servants with lanterns into the woods and hunted for Maggie himself, still dressed in his pajamas and silk robe, but she seemed to have disappeared. Elaine fell into such a violent fit of weeping and wailing that Paul summoned a doctor from Nanty-Glo to treat her for hysteria.

In the morning, the gardener and his dogs found Maggie in a patch of boggy ground. She was burned black and brittle, unrecognizable except for the gold ring found on her charred skeleton.

They say that Maggie's death was too much for her mother to bear: Elaine went mad from grief. Eventually she had to be taken to a private sanitorium, where she spent the rest of her life locked in a small room, unable to speak or communicate in any way. Her pitiful cries of anguish ceased only when she slept. Years later, Paul quietly divorced her and remarried.

It was said that, when Maggie's body was being prepared for burial, it collapsed into a pile of ashes. No one knows where she was buried, or even if she was buried at all.

The best place to see Maggie's ghost is near the St. Charles Cemetery or in any of several clearings along the length of the trail, such as the one where we encountered her. Sometimes observers have seen only a ball of fire weaving between the trees in the forest; some have seen a ball of fire with a child's face in its center. In the great majority of sightings of this pathetic ghost, she appears like a normal child, like the image we saw, though she is sometimes seen suspended a few feet above the air.

Because I have seen Maggie three times now, I feel as if I know her. My heart goes out to her, struck down so young and in such a frightening manner, right before the eyes of her horrified mother. Sometimes I get the impression that Maggie manifests so often for a reason, as if she is trying to communicate something important to us, the living. After all, she was certainly trying to tell us something that afternoon we spotted her on the trail. What that something might be, however, is Maggie's secret.

MADAME LORRAINE'S SUGGESTIONS: *See "Fires in the Night" on page 57.*

THE BRIDE OF
BEULAH

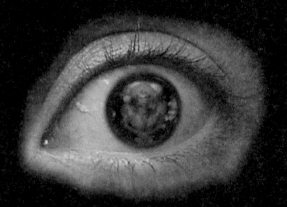

THE BRIDE OF BEULAH

NAME: *Josephine Rose Sheehy*

LOCATION: *Near mile marker five, adjacent to the new park.*

MANIFESTATION: *Fairly often, visual and auditory. Last reported sighting given by Eugene "Red" Lazkenski, who took the photographs that illustrate this section.*

WARNING: *This ghost is desperate to interact with you. Josephine manifests herself in different ways. You may see a white figure walking or floating toward you or away from you, or she might suddenly appear behind you on your bike, or follow you to your car and get in beside you. DO NOT RESPOND TO HER REQUEST FOR HELP. You cannot give her the help she craves, and answering her will only encourage her to badger you. Once she notices you, the best response is to ignore her. Turn your back on her if you can and go about your business as if she's not there.*

It was our second day on the trail. We had finished all our preparations and were one day ahead of the schedule. My parents, Patty and Walter, offered to buy us dinner at the Corner Restaurant in Belsano, and we took them up on it. The six of us got a booth in the rear of the restaurant, and I was just about to order when a squarely built woman of forty or so approached me. She was dressed in a white nurse's uniform and lab coat. I surmised she worked at Laurel Crest Retirement Home, since the badge pinned on her lapel bore that name.

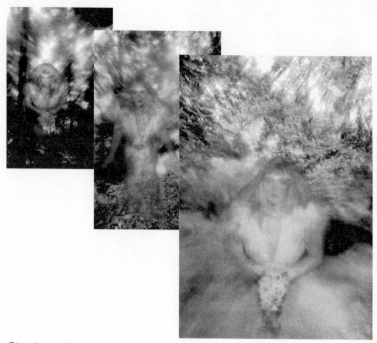

She introduced herself simply as Jane, adding that she wished to remain anonymous.

"I saw something really strange on the trail yesterday." The woman looked about the room, then lowered her voice as she slid onto the bench next to me. "So did my friends." She pointed out the window. Four women—all smoking cigarettes—were standing next to a blue Ford sedan. One of the women, with a large bandage on her forehead, waved at me and smiled a nervous but friendly smile.

"They don't want anyone to know about it. They think people will think they're crazy like…." Her voice trailed off and her face turned slightly red.

"Like us?"

"Well, a lot of folks around here think this whole thing about looking for ghosts is crazy. Not that they don't exist, but why look for them? I mean, you know the story of Maggie?" I nodded. "Well, everyone in town has seen her ghost, but nobody talks about it or tries to find her. Point is, she's dead. Never hurt no one. So why not leave her alone?"

There was some wisdom in letting sleeping ghosts lie, I thought. But if we didn't try to document them, we might never find out why the ghosts were there in the first place. It was true that they all seemed to die tragically, but lots of people die horrible deaths and never come back to haunt the living. I figured that the Ghost Town Trail ghosts must have left some unfinished business, and I began to wonder what kind of unfinished business Maggie had to take care of.

My thoughts were interrupted when Jane, who had been talking while I was daydreaming, whispered in my ear. "It was floating."

"What was?"

"The crystal ball, of course. Weren't you listening? We were about a quarter of a mile from the start of the trail when this big glass ball appeared. It was floating in the air, jouncing along about three feet from the ground, as if someone was carrying it one step at a time. It came straight for us, then rose in the air about another two feet and hit poor Barbara in the head." She glanced out the window at the bandaged woman. "Almost knocked her unconscious."

"Do you think we can persuade Barbara to give us her first-hand account?" I asked, hoping that someone would corroborate Jane's story.

"I don't think so. She's afraid. She said she's never going on the trail again until someone finds what hit her."

"What do you think hit her?"

"The crystal ball," she said, staring at me. "You haven't been listening at all, have you? I get it. You don't believe me."

"I didn't say I that." Actually, I was wondering if Jane or Barbara had seen a ghost behind that crystal ball, but I didn't want to put any ideas in their heads.

"I guess you want someone to end up in the hospital or worse before you investigate. Some ghostologist you are!" She got up from the bench and stalked out of the restaurant before I could stop her, carrying her wounded honor like a banner.

"Order me a soy burger, everything except pickles or onions," I instructed my mother, then followed the frazzled nurse outside. She had lit up a cigarette and was pacing back and forth, along with the other four. "She doesn't believe me," she told her friends.

"I knew she wouldn't," Barbara said, opening the car door. "Let's go."

"Wait a second, please," I said, approaching Barbara. "I do believe you. If you want me to help you, you're going to have to trust me. I need to know what you saw and felt. The same goes for the rest of you."

The women grew silent, then Jane asked if they could have a few minutes alone to discuss their situation in private. I nodded and returned to the restaurant just as the waitress arrived with everyone's order but mine.

"What was that all about?" Chelley asked as I sat down. Her dark gray eyes were lit with the glow of curiosity.

"I think there's a new ghost on the trail."

I looked out the window and watched as Jane, Barbara and the rest of the women piled into the car and drove off. I concluded that they did not want to wear the same label as us. Crazy.

The next day, Saturday June 10, we added the floating crystal ball to our list of sightings. I warned the crew to be on the lookout for any poltergeist activity, since flying objects were the hallmark of these troublesome spirits. While it wasn't normal for poltergeists or other ghosts to intentionally inflict injury on a living being, a few such cases have been documented. (For example, when I was working on the French Ghosts case, I interviewed a young woman who claimed to have been bitten on the neck by a passionate spirit, and had the bite marks to back up her story.)

"If you see the ball, don't try to film it," I instructed everyone. "Just get back to camp ASAP. Of course, it would be nice to validate Jane's claims, but I don't want anyone to get hurt." I consoled myself with the thought that we could measure the level of spectral activity with our infrared equipment before sending in the camera crew.

As planned, we set out into the woods to search for the ghost of Dean Maggio, an eighteen-year-old boy who shot himself in the head and had been spotted several times on the trail near mile marker three. We didn't find or see anything that day or the next, Sunday, June 11. It was more than a little depressing. On Monday we decided to give up on Dean and began looking for Joey Pudinsky, the ghost of a kid who was supposedly kidnapped by a horde of snakes about a mile down the trail. No luck. Feeling very low, we trudged back to home base at the edge of Mr. And Mrs. Polasky's property, a short walk from Vintondale.

A gray cloud hung over us, and it wasn't just the result of our disappointment. An actual thundercloud had moved in, bringing buckets of rain with it. I was thinking of moving everyone into a hotel, but then I reasoned it would detract from the spirit of the investigation, so to speak. So the four of us huddled together in my tent, poring over documents and personal testimonies. We were engaged in a heated debate over which ghost to pursue next when an elderly gentleman wearing a clear plastic rain bonnet poked his head into the tent.

"You the ghost people?" he asked. We must have answered that question a thousand times in the last couple of days. "I read about you in the *Nanty-Glo Journal*. I have a ghost for you."

This sounded encouraging, though I was somewhat wary of a man wearing women's headgear. "What ghost is that?" I asked, motioning for him to come in.

He entered the tent and removed the rain bonnet. "My wife's," he said stuffing the bonnet into the pocket of his jacket. "Couldn't find my umbrella." He sat down on my rolled-up sleeping bag. "My name's Gene Lanzenski, but you can call me Red." Our surprise visitor proceeded to tell us the best news I had heard since we had started our investigation. "I live right next to the trail. It practically runs through my backyard. We hear people talking and laughing all the time. You kind of get used to it. It's better than listening to the train wreck."

"Do you mind if I tape this?" I asked, pointing to my recorder.

"Go ahead. Never been taped before," he said, clearing his voice. "Well, once," he corrected himself. "My wife taped me snoring. I'm pretty loud. Anyhow, as I was saying, I have a ghost for you. A little over a year ago I was sitting on my back porch, having a cigarette. I'm not allowed to smoke in the house since we're taking care of our grandson. It was around nine o'clock and the sun had all but set, when I saw a woman in a long white dress walking on the trail toward Vintondale. Scared the bejeebers out of me at first. Then I realized it was probably some kids playing tricks. You know how kids are. I saw her a few more times, always around nine o'clock and always in the same spot. I told my friend, Hams Clairson. He worked at the mills with your dad," he said pointing to me. I nodded, remembering that I had met him once or twice.

"We decided to set a trap for the kid, to teach her a lesson about scaring people, so we waited in the nearby woods,

hoping for this jokester to show up, but she never did. The next night I kept watch alone behind a mountain laurel bush. I had set the alarm on my watch for nine a'clock and as the buzzer sounded, the lady in white appeared, right on cue. She stood staring at the bush. I crouched down as low as I could get, but she seemed to see me. She reached her hands out toward me and asked, 'Can you help me?' I got up from my hiding place and asked who she was and what she was doing there so late at night, but she just said, 'Can you help me?' again, and then, 'Please help me.' She sounded real pitiful, and I felt sorry for her. But as I started to walk toward her, I noticed she was floating above the ground and that I could see my porch light shining right through her. I started to scream and ran across the trail to my house. She followed me all the way to my back door, saying 'Can you help me? Please help me,' over and over."

Red stopped his story to take a quick smoke outside the tent. I watched through the opening in the flap as the rain fell on his wife's rain bonnet.

"Mighty peculiar man," Tricia commented, as she leafed though an old Bible searching for Maggie's family tree. "Good story, though."

"Ain't no story," Red said as he re-entered the tent. "It's God's honest truth, but I don't blame you for not believing me. Hams didn't believe me either. He told our poker buddies that I had finally lost my mind, and I took a hell of a ribbing for weeks until I showed them this."

Red handed me a photograph of a young lady in a white wedding gown, who appeared to be transparent. She was floating about a foot off the ground. "This is what I saw. Yessir, I knew I wasn't crazy."

I could feel my jaw begin to sag open and I quickly clamped it shut. I could barely contain my excitement. Here was the kind of documentation we had been hoping for! "Where did you get this picture?" I asked, holding it close to a portable lamp that rested on a stack of books that served as my nightstand.

Red lifted his head with the pride of authorship. "I took it, and I didn't doctor it up either. That's the real McCoy."

I passed the photograph to Chelley. The rest of the group gathered around to take a look.

"I waited for her in the evening behind them damn bushes for a whole week, but never saw her," Red explained. "Then I caught a glimpse of her far off, going around a bend in the trail. I ran after her but lost sight of her, so I walked that trail for three weeks straight, searching for her. Sunset to sunrise, looking for that dumb ghost. My wife thought I was nuts. Even called the doctor about me. She'd like to have me committed, not that I blame her. I'm still a bit of a drinker, you know, and sometimes I do see things. But that ghost was there. I didn't hallucerate…hullcinerate…imagine her."

"I'm sure you didn't," I murmured. "Do you mind if I keep this for a couple of days so Chelley can look it over thoroughly?"

Red nodded. "Sure. Heck, keep it. I had doubles made. Got lots of pictures of her. Want to see them?" He reached into the huge pocket of his red and black plaid hunting coat and pulled out a yellow envelope stuffed with black and white photographs. "Here they are," he said, handing me the envelope. I looked through the pictures. There were another 23 photos of the white lady, some close up, some at a distance, a few showing her from the back. "Have any idea who she is?" Red asked.

Chelley reached for the photographs. "She looks vaguely familiar to me," she said. "Give me a few minutes to think about this." She studied the pictures, then grabbed a file from the wooden crate and began rifling through a stack of old papers and photos. "Hey!" Chelley rubbed her arms, as if struck by a sudden attack of chills. "Look at this!" We all gathered around Chelley as she laid Red's picture and an old photograph of a young woman side by side on my sleeping bag. The women were identical.

"Mr. Lanzenski," I said, "I think we can say with some certainty that the ghost of Josephine Rose Sheehy, also known as the Bride of Beulah, has taken a liking to you."

"Well, I'll be," Red whispered softly. "I still got the old charm, even if it only works on dead women."

We all chuckled. Red had made our day. We hadn't had any reports of the Bride of Beulah manifesting on the trail, although we were all familiar with her story. Her main haunt was on Beulah Road, a country lane that connects Nanty-Glo with Ebensburg. It seemed as though Josephine had relocated to the trail.

"How'd the old girl die?" Red asked, sitting down next to me. "Pretty thing, ain't she?" He brushed his fingers over one of the photos as if he were touching the most delicate porcelain. It looked as though Red were falling in love, which was a potential danger facing all men who encountered Josephine. Even in death she was still beautiful, enchanting and sweetly innocent. There were rumors that a local man so loved this ghost that he committed suicide in hopes of joining her after death. However, Josephine was loyal to only one man—her fiancé, Robert John Kelly.

Like many ghostly histories, hers was tragic. Her mother was making last-minute alterations on Josephine's wedding gown the night before she was to wed Robert, her childhood sweetheart. Suddenly Josephine collapsed on the floor, holding her hands to her chest. She began to sob, saying, "Robbie, don't leave me," over and over. At that very moment, Robert, who was across town having a drink with Orin Zoroni, his best man, died instantly from an aneurysm of the heart.

Orin raced to Josephine's house to find her on the sofa, only partially recovered from her strange attack. He broke the

bad news to her as gently as he could. "He died with your name on his lips," Orin told Josephine.

Through her tears, she smiled a peaceful, accepting smile. "When I die, his name will be on my lips," she said. Before anyone could stop her, Josephine rose, raced to the study and grabbed a hunting knife from her father's collection. Orin was right behind her, half a moment too late to prevent her from plunging the sharp blade deep into her heart. "Robbie," she whispered as her legs buckled under her. She was dead when she hit the floor.

Josephine's desperate attempt to reunite with her dead love was unsuccessful. Instead, she doomed herself to walk the night dressed for the wedding that never took place, searching for Robert, who calls to her upon the wind, helplessly trying to guide her into his presence. Although others have heard Robert's plaintive voice, apparently Josephine cannot.

Red stood up and got ready to leave. "I would say it's been nice talking to you ladies," he said, "except that this is such a sad story. Glad I could help you out, anyway." He sighed deeply. "Wish I could help Josephine-Ghost, too," he said, shaking out his rain bonnet. He paused, as if looking into himself, and I realized the story had touched him more deeply than I had expected.

After a few moments, Red addressed me in a voice brimming with hope. "When my wife and I got married, my mother gave us a quilt that her mother gave to her. The pattern on it is a bunch of connecting rings. My wife calls it our wedding blanket. Do you think it'd help Josephine if I chiseled two interlocking rings on a rock at the place I first saw her? Maybe it will help bring those two together."

"That's a very romantic thought, Red," I said, smiling at him. Just then I saw him in an entirely new light.

"Well, I'm a romantical type of guy, y' know." He whipped the plastic bonnet onto his head and ducked out of the tent.

MADAME LORRAINE'S SUGGESTION:
Madame Lorraine has never seen this ghost. Nevertheless, she was very familiar with this story, which has been recounted by many people over the years. She agrees with Red, that interlocking rings may be a powerful healing symbol for these lost lovers. Since not everyone on the trail will have tools for chiseling or drawing, Madame suggests that you touch your thumbs and forefingers together to make two circles, then unite the circles to form the image of interlocked wedding rings. The image should look like this: Then say the words, "Best wishes, Josephine and Robert," addressing them as if they were already married. Madame Lorraine feels that this combination of actions will help unite the two ghosts and thus hopefully put them to rest.

GLORIA

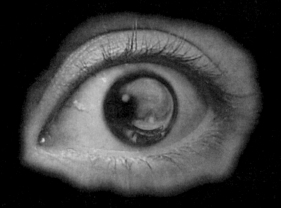

GLORIA

Hey, ghostbuster!"

I opened one eye. My father, who is the town's messenger, errand boy and taxi cab driver, was standing in my tent beside my cot in almost total darkness. I assumed he had a message for me, but I was pretty sure I didn't want it. Not before sunrise, anyway. "You up?" he whispered.

"Now I am," I answered, glancing at my alarm clock. I wasn't particularly surprised that he would be waking me up at five in the morning. My mother and he had this thing about getting me up early, ever since my first day in grade school. "Where's the fire?"

"Remember Jane, the nurse?" Dad was still speaking in a whisper, though I don't know why. "The one whose friend Barbara got beaned by a ghost-ball or something?" I nodded, groaning. It was too early to think about ghosts and indignant nurses. "Well, Jane stopped by last night on her way home from the second shift. She and Barbara have changed their minds and want you guys to meet them and the other girls near The Cut at eight o'clock this morning."

I rolled over on my side. "Why so early?" I pulled the covers over my head.

"Hey, hey!" My father gently pulled the blanket from my head. "Listen up, now. Jane has to be at work by three in the afternoon and she has to do the wash and go grocery shopping before that. C'mon! I got you another ghost. I thought you'd be happy."

"I'm happy, I'm happy," I moaned. I knew there was no use in arguing. My father had already agreed to the meeting.

"That's it, get up," he commanded, shaking me lightly. "I'll get the others moving, too. Your mother is making you all breakfast. Strawberry blintzes, heavy on the strawberries."

"That's not fair!" My dad knew that my mother's blintzes were the one thing that could coax me out of bed at five in the morning. I pulled myself out of the cot with all the speed and grace of a slug. "I'm not going to forget this," I said to my father, but he was already gone. I could hear the groans and yawns of the others waking up as I got dressed. I knew that once they had experienced one of my mother's famous breakfasts they would forgive this early morning intrusion. Plus, we would all get a chance to take a nice, hot shower.

Stuffed, refreshed and reasonably alert, we arrived at a widened area near the start of the trail, referred to by the locals as "The Cut", around five minutes to eight. Jane and her friends were sitting on rocks by the road, enjoying a breakfast of coffee and glazed donuts from Sheetz. Cigarette smoke hung around them like a foul-smelling fog. I noticed that Barbara no longer wore a bandage, but the lump on her head was still quite prominent.

We exchanged somber greetings, then got down to business. All eight of us walked in silence for about a quarter of a mile toward Vintondale, and when we reached a bench on the side of the trail, Barbara asked us to stop. "This is where that damn crystal ball whacked me on the cranium," she said, stamping her foot in the dirt near one end of the bench. "It appeared out of nowhere, just hanging in the air like a balloon, but it wasn't a balloon. Denise here thought it was an alien or something...."

"UFO," Denise corrected her.

"...But Jane got it right. She said, 'It's that glass thingie you see your future in,' and that's when that damn ball reared back and did this." Barbara pointed to the tennis-ball-sized lump on her forehead. "Major contusion. It shoulda hit Jane," she grumbled. "She's the one who called it a 'thingie.'"

The crew and I were absorbed in Barbara's story and the sight of the goose egg on her head. If she were putting us on, she was doing a bone-chilling job of it.

All of a sudden Chelley gasped in fear, then Tricia, then Joe and the rest of us reacted in kind. We all began to inch our way backward down the trail. A ghost holding a crystal ball and wearing a black shawl was walking toward us. "Hello! I'm not a ghost," a melodic voice called out to us.

"It could be a trick," Barbara whispered. "Look! She's got the ball." Barbara grabbed onto Jane, who was clutching Tricia like a tick on a hound. "Watch out! She might throw it!"

I swallowed my fear in one big gulp that nearly choked me. "Halt! Who are you and what do you want?" I demanded in a quavering voice. As a kid, I'd watched enough old army movies with my Dad to know that this was the approved way of confronting intruders.

"My name is Lorraine Siskin. I'm called Madame Lorraine. Please, don't be afraid. I came to find Gloria." The woman stopped for a moment, then continued walking. She seemed to grow bigger with every step she took toward us.

"There are no Glorias here," I answered. Rethinking that position, I turned and whispered to the group, "Are there?"

The nurses shook their heads. Even if one of them had been a Gloria, she surely would have never admitted to it.

"I know that," the woman said, relentlessly pressing forward. "Gloria's dead."

Well, that sent the less experienced of us fanning out into the edge of the woods.

I am proud to say my crew and I stood our ground in the face of the oncoming apparition. Joe started filming, Chelley began snapping pictures, Tricia turned on the infrared equipment and I flicked on my tape recorder. We were capturing every spectral movement.

"Great stuff you have there," the entity said, still approaching. "Where's the ghost?" Then she broke into peals of laughter.

The infrared meter, I noticed, was at dead zero.

We all became a little sheepish, especially the nurses who had sidled into the woods and now came sidling back. It seemed our "ghost" was really a live person, Madame Lorraine, a well-respected medium from Johnstown. She came to assist us in finding Gloria, the owner of the crystal ball. Gloria, according to the medium, was a not-so-well-respected, but very dead, psychic from Twin Rocks. Although generally unsuccessful, Gloria had shown a great deal of uncontrolled talent that Madame Lorraine was helping her to harness. To Gloria's surprise, her powers improved so much that she had begun receiving psychic clues to the identity of a man who had committed a murder in Twin Rocks. Gloria supplied the police with information, but shortly afterward turned up dead. It was Madame Lorraine who had found her body.

"She was a good friend of mine," Madame Lorraine concluded, "and I miss her terribly. This is her shawl," she said, touching the black scarf around her neck, "and this is her crystal ball, the very item that struck her dead. "

"See? I told you that thing was dangerous," Barbara blurted out. "It went and killed somebody. Where did Gloria cash in her chips? Here on the trail?"

Madame Lorraine smiled gently and shook her head. "The circumstances of Gloria's death are quite different than those of your injury," she said in her tuneful voice. "The real ball, here, is harmless in my hands. The spectral ball that assaulted you is the embodiment of the negative energy responsible for Gloria's violent death."

The medium approached Barbara and, with the nurse's consent, began to examine the sizable swelling. "Gloria is very sorry about what happened to you," Madame Lorraine continued. "She sometimes loses control of the spectral ball."

"Great," Barbara groaned. "A murder weapon with a mind of its own."

Madame Lorraine smiled again. "I think the ball's murdering days are over, although it still has a temper. The good news is that Gloria and I have been trying to get a clear line of communication for some time now, and I think, through your lump, we can do it."

"Start those cameras up again," I instructed Joe and Chelley, sensing that a possible manifestation was in the works.

Poor Barbara covered her forehead with her hands. "Is this going to hurt?"

"Not at all," Madame Lorraine assured her. "You see, I am virtually certain that, when the ball struck you, a tiny speck of protoplasm on its surface became imbedded in the tissue of your head. If that speck is still there, I can use it to facilitate communication with my late friend."

"Protoplasm? Do you mean plasma?" one of the nurses asked.

"Plasma is from people," I explained. "Protoplasm is from ghosts." I took the infrared meter from Joe and held it up to Barbara's noggin. "This device measures heat from otherworldly entities," I explained. I was about to say more when the needle on the meter shot up to the maximum level and remained there, pinned.

No one spoke for several seconds. Then Barbara, her eyes screwed shut, murmured, "Madame Lorraine?"

"Yes?"

"Get this thing outta me!"

Without any further delay Madame Lorraine went to work. After asking for total silence from everyone, she placed both hands on Barbara's swollen head and began summoning her dead apprentice. I was intrigued to see that the medium did not

go into a trance or follow any type of ritual. She addressed Gloria as if the woman were on one side of a locked door and Madame Lorraine on the other. "Gloria! Are you in there? Can you hear me?" she said in a soft but urgent tone.

Her exhortations continued for a full five minutes, as Chelley took pictures, Joe filmed the event, and I ran the tape recorder. All of us were spellbound, and Barbara was positively frozen. I didn't think it was possible for anyone to grit her teeth for so long. I was just beginning to doubt the truth behind Madame Lorraine's reputation when a thin mist began to rise from her hands and curl overhead. No one spoke or even gasped aloud. We were all too mesmerized. As I watched, the mist settled to the ground and shaped itself into the image of a woman, younger than Madame Lorraine, her hair bound in a scarf and her arms swathed in silver bangles that jingled like bells as she crossed her arms.

"There you are, Miss Gloria," Madame Lorraine said softly, removing her hands from Barbara's shivering head. "How good to see you again. I am so sorry about your untimely demise, dear. Would you like to talk about it?"

Thus the mystic and her deceased friend proceeded to hold one of the most bizarre conversations I've ever witnessed. I could hear every word that Madame Lorraine said, and I could see Gloria move her lips, change expressions, and gesture vividly as she spoke, but I couldn't hear a syllable of Gloria's speech. The scene reminded me of our silent encounter with Maggie's ghost. I turned the volume on my tape recorder to maximum, even though I knew it was hopeless to try to capture this exchange. From the puzzled looks on the faces of the people around me, I knew that they too were hearing a one-sided conversation.

"I've long suspected that your death was not an accident, as the coroner had ruled, but a murder," the medium said. Gloria's ghost nodded vigorously and worked her lips in silent speech. "Ah, then it's true. I thought your murderer just might be the man the police were seeking, and I'm glad to discover that I was right. Do you know his identity?"

Here Gloria's ghost pointed to the nearby bench and said something to Madame Lorraine. "She wants us to walk over to the bench," the medium said to us, barely able to conceal her excitement. The ghost blinked out, as if she had been turned off by a switch, and reappeared just as abruptly, kneeling on the ground at one end of the bench. Before her on the bench was a crystal ball, sitting on a metal stand.

We gathered around the bench, but not too closely. "There's that stinkin' ball," Barbara hissed as she slipped behind me and peered over my shoulder at the ghostly scene. I guess she thought that if anyone deserved to get brained again, it was the loony ghostologist who had stirred up all the spirits in the first place. "My head hurts just looking at it."

I felt as if I were in a trance. I wasn't alone. Everyone's sight was fixed on the kneeling apparition. Only Chelley, who went on snapping pictures, seemed to have any presence of mind left.

Gloria spread her hands over the ball, consulting it, per- haps. Slowly she raised her head to look at Madame Lorraine and began to mouth a word. What happened next took place in an instant. To my horror, the crystal ball rose in the air, as if plucked from its stand by some hidden force, and hurtled toward the medium. Startled, Gloria looked up. A silent scream contorted her face as she lifted her hands, trying to ward off the oncoming sphere. Immediately, like a bursting bubble, both ball and psychic disappeared.

For a long time no one said anything. Then Madame Lorraine turned to me. "Did you take pictures? Did you record her words?"

I replied that Chelley had taken some photos, but that I was pretty sure no one had heard Gloria but Madame Lorraine her- self.

"Hey! Look!"

I spun around in the direction of the voice. "My goose egg's gone! Thanks, Madame Lorraine." It was Barbara. The lump on her head had completely deflated, leaving only a red mark on her forehead the size and shape of a quarter.

"Better'n ice," one of the nurses muttered. "Wish I could do that."

This time, when Joe held the meter up to Barbara's injury, the needle didn't budge off the zero mark. "It's finished," Madame Lorraine breathed, though I didn't know if she was referring to the protoplasm or her contact with her late protégé. She looked pale, almost faint, so I had her sit down on the bench and sip some water I had brought with me.

"Gloria was trying to tell me the name of the man who murdered her," Madame Lorraine said, when she had recovered a little. "I'm sure she was."

"It looked to me like she said 'ma' or something,'" I offered. "Did you hear her actually say a name?"

Madame Lorraine looked at me in the cosmically penetrating way that only a true medium can look at another person who isn't. "Ahh…no," she said. "Unfortunately not. Maybe she did make the sound of the letter 'm'. I'm not sure." This didn't sound like a psychic speaking. It occurred to me that Madame Lorraine might be hesitant to reveal anything she had learned about the identity of the murderer, lest she put us in danger.

As if to confirm this possibility, Jane walked up beside me and tapped my shoulder. "We didn't see anything, right?" Behind her stood her fellow nurses, all shaking their heads in hearty denial of the incredible, incriminating scene they had just witnessed. "We know nothing, and if anybody asks us

about what happened, that's what we're going to say, okay? 'We know nothing. We saw nothing.'"

"Nothing, nothing, nothing," Denise echoed.

That sounded good to me. I didn't see any reason for these angels of mercy to get mixed up in a murder mystery and put themselves in any more danger than they already had. "What are you talking about?" I said. "Nothing happened, so of course you saw nothing. Absolutely nothing, except some loco ghost-busters stumbling around the woods, looking in vain for lost souls. And I suggest you get out of here quickly, before nothing happens again and hits somebody else on the head."

Jane and her companions took the hint. They did an about-face in unison and began striding rapidly back to the parking lot, as though they had been called to help a patient in ICU. While Chelley, Joe and Tricia packed up their equipment, I made small talk with Madame Lorraine. I was positive that Gloria had managed to relay something to her, and I had no doubt that this was not the last communication between the two psychics. I also knew that, when she had gleaned sufficient evidence to build a case against someone, Madame Lorraine wouldn't lose any time taking it to the police. I only hoped that some day justice would be done and Gloria could rest in peace.

"You know, your skills are very impressive," I told her as we sat on the bench where Gloria had materialized only minutes earlier. "We're trying to document...."

The medium nodded. "Yes, I know why you're here and what you're doing. Why else did you think I showed up here at this ungodly hour in the middle of the woods? Now, I know that Gloria isn't the only restless spirit on this trail, and I applaud your efforts to unveil their stories. Tell me, would you like me to assist you with your endeavors?"

"Yes, please," I answered, with a grateful sigh. "We could benefit a lot from your help."

Madame Lorraine smiled and stood up, tucking the crystal ball under one arm. "Benefit from my help?" she asked. "My dear, you positively require it."

When I asked her if there were anything we could do to help Gloria, she paused for a moment, then touched the middle of my forehead with her index finger. "That, Miss Cynthia," she said, "is a lovely idea. I'm not sure what can be done to help Gloria, but I know there are a lot of other spirits out there, yearning for release from their earthly prisons. I'd be glad to give advice to you and all travelers on the trail who seek to free lost souls."

Although she didn't know it at the time, the medium had just created Madame Lorraine's Suggestions and Comments. Kindly reviewing all the stories in this book, Madame Lorraine offered her counsel, where appropriate, which appears at the end of most of the tales.

Thus Madame Lorraine became an unplanned but indispensable part of crew, our investigation and the volume you are now reading.

MADAME LORRAINE'S SUGGESTION: *We all have a talent that is unique to us. The key is to mine your precious stone, make the necessary cuts, polish the jewel and wear it proudly. This is what Gloria was in the process of doing. Learn by her example and you will honor her as well as yourself.*

THE LANTERN
MAN

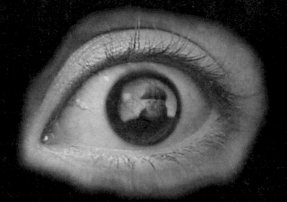

THE LANTERN MAN

NAME: *George Billings*

LOCATION: *Can be spotted on the left-hand side of the first bridge on the trail from Twin Rocks to Vintondale. The apparition appears to be standing on old railroad ties near the stream.*

MANIFESTATION: *Fairly often since the old Cardiff Bridge was demolished. George, a stocky man with a thick head of hair and a concerned expression, is always seen with his old-fashioned lantern, whose candle is always lit. Several motorists on Route 271 have reported seeing just his lantern, which appeared as a ball of light swaying back and forth among the trees. Last seen June 15, 2000.*

Adjacent to Twin Rocks is the tiny village of Cardiff. Only a handful of people still live there, in small, neatly-kept houses. Cardiff is a Brigadoon, a place where time has stopped. For me, every visit back to the town brings a flood of happy childhood memories. It is the hometown of my father's family and the former haunt of George Billings, The Lantern Man. The first memory I have regarding this ghost is rather sketchy, though I recall that my older cousins used to frighten me with stories about phantom lights appearing in the forest at night. My parents did not like me repeating George's story. They thought his daughter would be hurt to hear people telling tales about her father being a ghost.

Therefore, I was both surprised and delighted when George's daughter, Esther, contacted me. She was a small,

dark-haired woman of sixty or so. The light of her vivacious personality radiated from her face. She had heard I was compiling information about the ghosts who had moved to the Ghost Town Trail and wanted me to include her father's story in my book. Reports of a man holding a lantern near the first bridge on the trail began within hours of the Cardiff Bridge being torn down.

We were ten days into our investigation when I interviewed Esther on a bench on the trail from Twin Rocks to Vintondale. She asked that her picture not be shown in the book, although she did allow us to take a few shots of her for use as documentation for our personal files.

"You really had to know my father to appreciate what a wonderful man he was," she began, almost in a whisper. "He was kind to a fault. Everyone who knew him thought so. He was always helping people. In fact, that's what he was doing the night he was killed, November 7, 1950. It was my birthday, you know."

"I'm sorry," I said. The pain of losing her father some fifty years ago still shone in her eyes. I could only imagine what it must have felt like to have someone you adored leave you so abruptly, and on your special day, no less.

"Your father is still alive?" she asked. I nodded. "In good health?"

"The doctors don't think so, but he thinks he's twenty and acts like he's twenty." I smiled as a few of my father's recent antics crossed my mind.

"Then he is twenty," she stated, a look of wisdom on her face. "If you believe something, then it's true, isn't it?"

"I suppose so."

She paused a moment, her gray eyes downcast, as if concentrating on the gravel at her feet. Then she looked up, straight into my face. "Your ghosts are real to you, aren't they? It doesn't matter to you how many people don't believe in them." She crossed her hands and rested them on her lap. Her point was made. "I have never seen my father's ghost, although I have heard tales of people who have claimed to. Still, I know people can be mean sometimes, making up stories to scare the young and impressionable. Nevertheless, I believed. Until they tore the Cardiff Bridge down, I would visit the spot where my father died that cold night in November at least once a week. When I was younger I used to sneak out of my bedroom window and crouch under the bridge, waiting for him to come back. Of course, he never did, but a child doesn't give up hope so easily. A couple of times I thought I felt him near me as I sat in the darkness crying. For a few brief moments, I thought I heard his voice and smelled the Bay Rum aftershave he always wore. Was he really there? It might just as well have been wishful thinking." Again she fell silent for a few moments, and when she continued her voice was even softer. "Do you know how he died?" she asked, staring straight ahead.

"I've only heard stories," I answered, not wanting to get involved in the more gruesome aspects of the case. "They say that he stumbled and fell on the track and the train ran over him."

"Yes, that's true." Her voice trailed off and she seemed to take an interest in a bright red cardinal in a pine tree near the bench. After several seconds, Esther asked if I would like to see a picture of her father. She opened up a gold, oval locket that she wore on a chain around her neck. "My father gave this to me. It was my last birthday present from him. He told me that no matter what happened to him, as long as I wore this around my neck he would always be with me."

The black and white photograph revealed an unsmiling but handsome man with a shock of gray hair. George looked troubled, as if some terrible secret burdened his soul.

"His eyes were blue," she offered. "Like a robin's egg."

"He looks a bit like my own father," I offered, startled by the resemblance.

"Then we have something in common, don't we?" Esther took the locket from me and gave me a sad smile. "I hope you keep that in mind when you write this story. I don't want to come across as a sentimental old fool."

"Sentimental? For loving your father? Nobody would think that of you."

"I don't know," she sighed, rubbing her hands together, as people do when they're bothered by arthritis. "Sometimes I think it's possible to love someone too much. But I'm going off on a tangent, aren't I? I want you to know exactly what happened that night."

I listened intently as she went on with her story.

"Three weeks before my father died I overheard him telling my mother about a young lady he had seen walking the tracks around six o'clock in the evening, just as the 916 from Pittsburgh was coming around the bend. He was the lantern man whose job it was to signal the train engineers that they had safe passage through the town. He used to walk up and down the track, making sure it was clear of debris and, of course, people and animals. Then he would walk back to the bridge and wave his lantern to signal 'all clear' to the train. On that particular night, this woman was nearly run over by the train. Actually, my father thought she had been run over, but, since he never found her, he assumed she must have gotten away just in time.

"He saw her once more, only this time she spoke his name. This intrigued him, since he had no idea who she was. Someone traveling through, he guessed, or someone's relative on a visit. He said that she wore a silver dress that glowed in the moonlight, giving her an ethereal look. My mother jokingly warned him about what would happen to him if she found him flirting with any woman, of this world or not, but I could tell from the tension in their voices that they were both a little nervous over the whole thing. They believed in premonitions and such. It was said that my Aunt Emma saw a ghost, similar to the woman my dad described. After seeing it for the third time, she was struck by a car and died.

"Anyway, on the day he died, my mother was getting my birthday dinner ready. It was going to be a feast because I was, as my father said, "getting into the double digits." I was turning ten. All week he had gently teased me about not having enough money to buy me a birthday gift, so I knew whatever he bought me was extra special. Before he left that day, he came into my room and stood watching me play with a doll that my Aunt Lettie had sent me all the way from England.

"You're getting too big for dolls," he said. "It's time you got a grown-up gift." He brought his hand out from behind his back and handed me a small package wrapped in a square of white linen and tied with a bright pink ribbon.

"'Can I open it now, Papa?' I asked, looking at the gift as if it were a snowflake that would melt before I could examine it carefully.

"'I was going to wait until after the celebration,' he said, 'but I guess you should open it before I go and signal old 916.' Immediately I opened my precious gift, the one I showed you.

"'Now remember, honey," he said, as he turned to leave. 'You can depend on your Papa. I love you more than anything and I'm not ever going to leave you.'

"'And I'll never let you leave, Papa,' I promised, crossing my heart. It's my belief that my father had accepted that he was going to die that night and wanted to make sure that I knew how much he loved me. In any case, I waited up for him but he didn't come home. The sheriff came by in the morning and told us that my father must have tripped over a branch and fallen into the path of the 916. The train ran over him, cutting him in two. I was devastated, and so was my mother. She's in a nursing home now, but she believes to this day that my father's death was not an accident. She says that God had sent an angel to call him to Heaven, that it was his time."

Esther quit speaking and drew a deep, shuddering breath. A minute or two passed as she sat quietly picking at a splinter in the bench, and I waited patiently for her to continue. As suddenly as she stopped she began speaking again. "I hear that he has made this place his new home. Have you seen him?"

I shook my head. "No, but I have interviewed a couple of people who tell me they've seen someone on the trail in the evenings, holding a lantern. The description they give of the lantern man is very similar to that of your father."

"Well, I want to release him," she said, standing up. "And I hope you can help me."

I stretched out my hands in a gesture of helplessness. "I'd like to, but I'm not sure how I can. It would probably involve contacting him, and spirits generally show up when they want to. When they do, they reveal only what they want to. You can't force them into anything."

"But…but you're the ghost lady, right?" she sputtered, as if she hadn't heard me at all. "You must know how to help me."

We began walking back to the car, and in the meantime an idea had occurred to me. "Well, there is this woman. Madame Lorraine. A psychic." I told her a little about Madame Lorraine's astounding abilities to communicate with the spirit world. "Of course, I can't promise she'll agree to help you, and even if she does, nothing may come of it. Making contact with those who've crossed over isn't a stroll in the park, you know, even for the most talented medium."

Esther gave a heart-breaking little laugh. "Yes, I know. After all, I've been trying to release my father's spirit for the past fifty years without success, and it's beginning to wear me down. I think it's time I let someone else take a shot at it."

FIRES IN THE
NIGHT

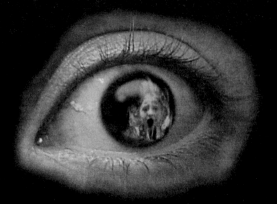

FIRES IN THE NIGHT

It was Tuesday, June 30th. The night sky was clear and the stars looked close enough to pluck. Madame Lorraine and Esther joined us for a meal of veggie hot dogs, fire-baked potatoes and corn and roasted marshmallows. My husband Tom, who drove up from Pittsburgh to spend a day on the trail with us, had brought along a few bottles of Merlot that we happily shared with one another. None of us knew, or could possibly know, that we were about to embark on the longest, most exhausting day of our ghost-seeking careers.

We all sat around the campfire, exchanging stories of our experiences with the "other world", talking philosophy and offering advice that was tinged with the effects of good wine. I felt more relaxed and at peace with myself than I had for a long time, and I realized this probably meant I was beginning to get in touch with my country roots.

Madame Lorraine and my husband were engrossed in a discussion about the symbolic nature of decks and fencing and their positive and negative influences on suburban communities. I found their conversation fascinating at the time, although to this day I cannot recall a single word of it. Esther turned out to be quite a party animal. She sang Frank Sinatra tunes with an Ethel Mermann twist, taught us all to polka and tutored Joe and Tricia in the fine art of yodeling.

It was approaching midnight when Madame Lorraine began telling us stories of her adventures as a medium.

"My skills came as something of a shock to my parents," Madame Lorraine told us, as she put another marshmallow on her long, pointed stick. "I was six years old when I suddenly announced that Mrs. Blankosky's cat was locked in Smith and Sons' meat wagon, which was on its way to the processing plant in Johnstown. Moments after my revelation, old Mrs. Blankosky came to our door asking if we had seen Puffman, her aged, bloated, but spirited gray cat. Hesitantly my mother told the weeping cat owner what I had said, implying that I had actually seen the cat enter the wagon. To our neighbor's relief, the Smith and Sons' driver found Puffman in the wagon, perfectly safe and stuffed full of pork kidneys.

"My parents gave me the third degree. Mrs. Blankosky even accused me of locking her cat in the wagon. That's when I learned to keep my premonitions to myself. I never spoke another word to anyone about my visions, my conversations with those who had passed over or the information I received from other people's angels. Those were sad days for me, knowing that I could help others but being terrified that I might be unfairly judged.

"Then one day I met Madame Zoe Candeni, The World's Greatest Medium, at the Cambria County Fair. I was a celebrating my twenty-first birthday with a bunch of my friends and, like you, Esther, I received a gift on my birthday that changed my life. I saw Madame Zoe sitting in a small, multi-colored tent, dressed all in black. A veil covered her face, except for her eyes that were dark and heavy with purple eye shadow. A pentagram had been painted in white on the center of her forehead." Madame Lorraine paused to eat a charcoaled marshmallow. "On every finger she wore a ring with a different colored stone, and her blouse was spangled with silver stars and crescent moons.

"My friends and I stood in front of the tent, trying to determine which one of us was brave enough to have our fortune told. When my comrades found out it was my birthday, they promptly shoved me into Madame Zoe's lair.

"'Happy birthday,' she said.

"'How did you know that?'" I asked in amazement.

"She laughed. 'The great Madame Zoe knows everything. Besides,' she added, 'I overheard your friends talking. Shall we look into the crystal ball, Miss Lorraine?' She lightly touched the iridescent glass ball that rested on a small tripod in the shape of three children holding hands in a circle. 'Or perhaps we should just consult with the sad-faced lady who stands so quietly behind you.'

"I sat in silence, shocked that she had seen the astral presence whom I call Mae. Back then, I thought of her as my private angel, though I later learned that she is my spirit guide. This was too much for me. 'I don't know what you're talking about,' I murmured at last, and made a feeble effort to leave.

"Madame Zoe stared me down. I remained seated, pinned by her dark, knowing eyes that seemed to penetrate my own. I felt strangely drawn to this woman, as if I had found a friend who understood my deepest secrets. She leaned over and patted my cheek. 'We will meet again at a more suitable time, my child. Go now. No charge.'

"We did meet again, about two months later. I was working as a rookie reporter for the *Johnstown Express* and was assigned to research and write a piece on a little boy who was missing. My first stop was to interview the Chief of Police, Earl Wagner. He was running late, so I patiently entertained myself by eavesdropping on prostitutes who were handcuffed to their chairs.

"The door to the chief's office swung open. 'Are you Lorraine Siskin from the *Express*?' a gray-haired, uniformed officer asked me. I nodded. 'Well, get in here.'

"When I walked into the room I saw a woman who looked vaguely familiar. Her long blonde hair was swept up into a French roll, and her navy blue wool suit fit her exactly right. Looking at her dashing, sophisticated figure made me feel uncomfortably conscious of my high school blazer and my slightly-too-short skirt.

"'This is Miss Browne,' Chief Wagner said. 'She's helping us find the missing boy. Whatever she has to say is off the record. The only reason you're here in the first place is because she asked that you be allowed to be a part of this investigation. You can have the exclusive story about our search for the boy, but you can't write anything about Miss Browne's involvement. Understood?"

I agreed. I was twenty-one, on the scent of my first big story, and I had no idea who Miss Browne was or what her involvement in the case might be.

Then she spoke. I knew immediately who she was. It was Madame Zoe, the World's Greatest Medium.

"'I am going to teach you to be true to yourself, Miss Lorraine,' she said to me, her dark eyes gleaming with delight at my silent recognition. 'And it will not be an easy journey, let me assure you.' Then she turned to face the chief. 'This, Chief Wagner, is the person who will take my place.'

"As it turned out, Madame Zoe located the missing child, who was found trapped in an abandoned coal mining shaft. He was barely alive when they pulled him out, but he lived to graduate from college, spend five years in the Peace Corps, and later become a presidential advisor in Washington, D.C.

"Chief Wagner got all kinds of accolades for his sharp detective work, though he certainly didn't deserve all of them. Madame Zoe? She was never mentioned in any of the media accounts. For the next two years I studied with her almost every evening, learning how to access the talents I had hidden deep within me ever since I was accused of shanghaiing that poor cat. When Madame Zoe retired to Sedona, Arizona, I became the head of the police department's missing persons office. It was at that point that I came to be called 'Madame Lorraine' instead of 'Miss'."

"Quite a résumé," I said, placing another log on the fire. "I'm sure that you have more than enough credentials to help our own dear Esther find the answer to the question she has for you."

Madame Lorraine already knew most of Esther's story. She asked her only one question. "Are you ready to let go?"

Esther answered that she would do whatever it might take to release her father.

"You already know the answer to what you seek," Madame Lorraine said. "It is all a matter of doing. That locket you wear is the key that will turn the lock and open a new doorway for both you and your father."

Esther smiled as if she understood exactly what Madame Lorraine was talking about.

"So you agree?" Madame Lorraine asked.

"I agree," Esther answered, slipping the necklace from her neck and placing it carefully in her handbag. "How about the day after tomorrow, just before dawn? The bridge."

"Perfect." The medium nodded knowingly.

"What's going on?" I asked, totally bewildered as to what was going to happen, where and why.

"You all should be a part of this," Esther said, standing up. "Please meet Madame Lorraine and me the day after tomorrow at the bridge where my father has been seen recently. It will all make sense to you, I promise."

"Does it have to be so early?" I said, regretting the whiny sound of my voice.

"I'm afraid so," Esther said with a sympathetic smile. "I want this to be private, but if we arrive after dawn the trail will be full of hikers and joggers. I have to go now, to say my final good-byes to my father."

I walked Esther to her car and was on my way back when I saw a terrifying sight. Long red flames were shooting skyward from the campfire, just as if someone had doused it with gasoline. I raced toward camp, nearly breaking my neck when I slid on some loose gravel by the side of the trail.

"What's happening here?" I shouted, out of breath, just as the fire began to die back down to normal.

Nobody said a word. Everyone was gazing spellbound at Madame Lorraine, their eyes as large and round as silver dollars. Silence hung in the night air like a shroud, disturbed only by the crackling of the fire. Madame Lorraine was peering straight into the flames, her concentration obviously focused inward on some world separate from our own. "Make no sud-

den movements," she whispered, closing her eyes. "Maggie is with us. I can see her face in the flames. She wants to talk to us, so I will attempt to access her thoughts and translate them into words."

I gasped, then examined the campfire carefully. Sparks flared. Could they be eyes? Was that jet of flame a mouth? I blinked and saw a face. The next instant I didn't. I decided just to trust Madame Lorraine and listen to her.

"I'm getting some clear contact now," she whispered, her eyes opening slightly. "I'll try to speak as myself, but don't be surprised if Maggie breaks through and addresses you in her own voice. Stay alert. Things might get a little confusing."

A few moments passed in silence, and then Madame Lorraine spoke again, her voice barely louder than it was before. "Her name is Magdalena Bronski-Stark," she said. "She says she doesn't want to be here in the Cold Nowhere. She's frightened, but she wants to tell us what really happened to her. Nobody knows, she says, but now they will. We must tell them."

A sudden chill settled like mist over the campsite. I shuddered. An odd odor filled the air, as though a piece of steak had fallen in the fire, although we hadn't been eating any meat. There wasn't the slightest doubt in my mind that I, too, was accessing the thoughts of Maggie's ghost.

"She says that the newspapers were all wrong when they said that her mama loved her," Madame Lorraine continued, her eyes now shut very tightly and her face taut with concentration. "It wasn't true. Her mother didn't even like her. She used to tell Maggie all the time how much she hated her."

Tears came to my eyes as I slowly understood the mental agony that Maggie must have endured.

"She said that Maggie's daddy wanted a boy," Madame Lorraine said, "and when Maggie came along, he left the family. Her mother said he had found another lady to love, and this was Maggie's fault. Whenever he visited, which wasn't often, he was always nice to Maggie, but he and her mama screamed and fought so much with each other that Maggie was afraid the house would fall down. She would start crying, and then her mama would get very angry. "

Madame Lorraine paused, breathing hard. Joe made a motion as if to rise and approach her, but the medium held up her hand to stop him, then began again. "Whenever Maggie's daddy left after a visit, her mother would take her into a room alone." Here Madame Lorraine raised her fist and brought it down violently, again and again, as if striking an invisible victim. "And she hit Maggie with her hand, then with a switch, then with a metal rod. Maggie was very frightened and hurting badly and couldn't stop crying. 'You'll land me in the poorhouse! It's all your fault!' her mother yelled at her.

"Maggie became black and blue all over. She was thin, too, because her mother gave her very little to eat, saying that Maggie wasn't worth feeding. She locked Maggie in a small room, which was cold, bare and dark and very frightening." Madame Lorraine's voice changed as she spoke, becoming high and thin. The campfire flames wavered, and this time I was certain I did see a girl's face in the fire. "I was afraid of rats coming into the room. I could hear them in the walls, and I used to cry all the time."

Madame Lorraine clenched her teeth, then relaxed and continued. "Two maids tried to help Maggie and told her they would summon the police, but the police never came, and then the maids stopped coming, too. Instead her mother came to her room one night, grabbed her wrist and pulled her down the stairs. The house was dark and silent, completely empty. Maggie was scared. Her arm hurt where her mother was holding it."

Madame Lorraine paused, frowning, and I could tell by her troubled expression that her contact with Maggie was putting an immense strain on her, physically as well as psychically. Sweat gleamed on her forehead. After a short while, she continued, shifting roles from medium to child as the little girl's spirit possessed her. "Maggie's mother waved some sort of paper in front of my face, but Maggie didn't know what it was. Her mother kept saying, 'He wants a divorce' over and over as she dragged her into the parlor, then the kitchen and then into the dining room. The big candelabra on the dining table was lit and all six candles were burning brightly. Maggie's mother bent over her, her face twisted in anger. Then she grabbed a candle from the candelabra and held it against my pinafore."

All four of us gasped at the same time. "That bitch!" Chelley muttered.

"Help! Help! I'm on fire!" Madame Lorraine cried out. This time Joe sprang to his feet and came up to Madame Lorraine, but again she held up her hand and gestured for him to sit down. "Maggie's leg and stomach started to hurt something awful. She felt very frightened and began to run. Someone had forgotten to lock the French doors in the sunroom. Maggie pulled them open and ran out into the garden. I was so scared! It hurt so bad! I ran into the woods. I ran and ran. Everywhere I looked it was hot and orange."

Here Madame Lorraine stopped and fell silent, as if waiting for more information. None of us spoke or even moved, although several minutes went by. At last the strange narration began again. "Then Maggie was in the air, looking down at some little black burned thing on the ground. She didn't hurt anymore. For a while she was too frightened to go back to the house, and when she did she saw her father and some other men help mama into a big black car. Her hair stuck out all over her head and her eyes looked red and wild. She wouldn't stop screaming."

Madame Lorraine paused. She pressed both hands against her temples, then sat very still for several seconds, her hands in her lap. The atmosphere was so charged with tension that I had the strange impression that reality would snap at any moment, like a rubber band stretched too tight, and the entire world would disappear with a pop!

"Maggie tried to get her father to notice her," Madame Lorraine continued at last. "When he didn't respond to her, she realized that she was dead. Maggie fled crying into the woods and wandered about there for days. She tried to enter St. Charles Cemetery to see where she was buried, but she could not get past the gates. She could walk through trees and walls, but not through the cemetery fence. Anger, sadness, loneliness, confusion—they all swarmed around her like flies.

"Maggie returned to the house one more time. Several servants she didn't know were gathered in the kitchen, talking about some story in the newspaper. She listened to them and found out that they were talking about her. The story in the newspaper said that Maggie had died because she dropped a candle on herself. When she heard this, Maggie felt anger build up inside her. She became very hot and soon saw that flames were shooting out of her body. Suddenly the servants shouted in alarm and ran up the stairs. Maggie went back to the woods. After that, whenever she saw anybody, she tried to tell them what happened, but nobody could hear her even when they saw her…"

Madame Lorraine face was chalk-white. She swayed to and fro, and for a moment I thought she was going to pass out. Then she seemed to draw on some inner source of energy and forced herself to remain still. "Then I found Madame Lorraine. I'm so happy that someone can hear me again."

All at once the medium slumped to the ground, as if she had been held up on wires that had been suddenly cut. We all jumped to our feet and hurried to her side. I feared the worst. Fortunately, Madame Lorraine was just a little faint, but she was very cold and shivering violently. Tom and I helped her into a sitting position and wrapped two blankets around her. Joe poured her a cup of wine and I held it for her as she took a few sips. "Are you okay?" I asked her softly. "Who...What...?"

"That was Maggie," Madame Lorraine whispered. The color slowly began to creep back into her cheeks. "That was her story, her real story."

"Oh, the poor little thing!" Chelley murmured, blowing her nose into a paper napkin.

"I hope Maggie's mother is dead," Joe growled, "because if she's not, I'll have to kill her."

"She's dead," Madame Lorraine said, tossing back half a cup of Merlot. "Hanged herself in the state sanitorium many years ago. Maggie's dad is dead too. He must have covered up the story to protect the family name. God knows he had enough money to bribe the newspaper publisher and the chief of police to keep things quiet for eighty years. Even her burial place remains a secret to this day."

Something troubled me about Madame Lorraine's words, but I decided to keep quiet. She'd experienced enough for one night. I lifted the wine bottle and filled the empty cup that quivered in her hand. "I can hardly believe it," I said. "For almost eighty years we've all been duped. I even wrote up that hideous lie for the book."

"If you wanted to add Maggie's true story to your book, Miss Cynthia," the medium said, "it surely couldn't do any harm."

The book! Why hadn't I thought of it sooner? I whirled about and pounced on Chelley like a wolf on a rabbit. "Did you get any of this on film?"

"Y…y…yes…n…n…no," her answer staggered back to me. "Just a few. I was too scared."

I was disappointed, but I sure could understand her reaction. "Don't worry about it," I said. Then I turned back to Madame Lorraine. "Do you think that Maggie's soul has been released, now that she's revealed the truth?"

"I don't know," Madame Lorraine said, removing a blanket from her shoulders. "Only time will tell for sure. If no sightings occur for a year or so, then the chances are good that she has been set free. Otherwise…." Without warning she fixed me with an icy look that made me squirm in discomfort. "There may be something that is still preventing her release," she added mysteriously.

Under the circumstances, I thought Madame Lorraine ought to get a good night's sleep, so I let her have my cot in the tent. There was only room for one to sleep in Tom's car, and he gallantly offered me the space, but I refused. "I'll be fine with a sleeping bag on the ground," I told him, and I really thought I would. Anyone who has ever tried to sleep on the bare, hard ground, however, can tell you that it makes the worst bed in the world. Not that I was about to enjoy much sleep that night. I couldn't get Maggie out of my mind.

I didn't remember falling asleep, but I do remember dreaming. I was picking blackberries in the strippings, and Maggie was with me. It was a glorious day. The sun was shining in a blue sky sprinkled with rainbows. The blackberries were as big as plums, and three fat little bluebirds hopped around us as we picked, warbling tunes from Broadway musicals.

Maggie told me one joke after another, and she almost never stopped laughing. After a while we started for home, carrying at least ten buckets full of berries apiece. Maggie had moved on to riddles, and the bluebirds flew over us, singing in harmony. But when we reached St. Charles Cemetery, the birds disappeared and Maggie's jokes ceased. She walked up to the entrance, set down her ten buckets, and pulled at the iron gates. Although they weren't locked, they refused to open.

"Help me, Cindy," she said, still rattling the gates. "I've got to go in."

"Aw, c'mon, silly," I chided her. "Get away from there. Let's go home. I'll show you all my toys, and my mom'll fix us some berry cobbler."

"No, I've got to go in," Maggie replied, her voice edged with desperation. "I've just got to go in. Won't you please help me?"

"Okay," I said. Immediately I was awake, my back aching and my legs as stiff as iron. The sun was just beginning to rise over the Laurel Highlands, spreading a pink glow on the blue mountains. Once I picked myself up and satisfied myself that I was not permanently injured, I hobbled over to the tent where Madame Lorraine lay in comparative comfort. She was already awake, and when I looked at her, she nodded with enthusiasm.

"You're right," she said. "Maggie can't enter the cemetery because she never received a Christian burial. Maybe her father thought that the undertaker might discover the truth behind the tragedy. In any case, it's not likely she'll rest in peace until someone acknowledges her death with some sort of holy rites."

"But...but...but I didn't even tell you my dream!" I blurted. "How did you know?"

Madame Lorraine shrugged. A ghost of a smile crossed her face. "You're the ghostologist," she said. "You tell me."

Then and there we formulated a strategy, and when everyone else awoke I told them that we were not going to search for Ron Celestine and his dismembered buddies, as we'd planned, but try to guide Maggie to a final resting place. Everyone was still moved by the occurrences of the night before and agreed that something had to be done to help the long-suffering child.

Using my cell phone and a telephone book borrowed from the Polaskys, I dialed up the number of the local Roman Catholic church and soon found myself knee-deep in conversation with one Father Matthew. "...And that's why we have to get her into that cemetery, Father, one way or another, " I finished up lamely, realizing I must have sounded like a lunatic. *He's probably in shock*, I thought. *Any second now he's going to consign me to Satan and slam down the phone.*

But oddly enough, Father Matthew was sympathetic, if not downright helpful. "No one can know for certain what happens to the soul in such bizarre situations," he said. "Come over as soon as you can, and I'm sure we can work something out."

He must be one of these new progressive priests, I thought. We lost no time driving down to the church and locating the broad-minded padre, who was in his office, coordinating a big bingo festival scheduled for later that month. Father Matthew was a round little man, neither old nor young, with a red bosun's beard and a booming voice that seemed distinctly out of place in a cathedral. He was also missing the tops of his middle, ring and pinkie fingers on his left hand. The deformity was so peculiar that I knew right away I shouldn't draw any attention to it.

Like everyone else in Twin Rocks, he had heard of Maggie, and the news of the true circumstances of her death saddened him. He had already sketched out an appropriate service for the little girl, complete with a eulogy and blessings in the cemetery itself.

"I'll be leaving town soon," I said, concerned about the timing. "When do you plan on holding the services?"

Father Matthew smiled and stretched out his arms wide. As he did so, he knocked over a stack of papers, just one of many that covered the desk and floor like an army of stalagmites.

"Oh, sorry!" he cried out as a white envelope sailed past my nose. "How about right now?" he said. "I'm free until the *angelus* this evening."

"Sounds good to me." Relieved, I followed the father into the sanctuary. I, the crew and Madame Lorraine piled into a front pew and listened enthralled as Father Matthew delivered a beautiful, touching and admirably concise memorial service for a child he had never seen. When he was finished, with tears still smarting in my eyes, I rose and folded a fifty-dollar bill into his hand. "Lovely, just lovely." I dabbed my nose with a tissue. "Now what, Father?"

"We shall proceed to the graveyard," he said, his deep voice ricocheting around the sanctuary walls. "I hope you're all wearing good walking shoes." As he passed a large vase of flowers in front of a statue of the Virgin Mary, he stopped and pulled two delicate pink roses from the elegant arrangement.

"What are those for?" I asked.

"For Maggie," he said simply, and led us all out into the churchyard.

St. Charles Cemetery was only a quarter mile from the church, but the path was full of stones and briars, and we were all exhausted when we arrived. Father Matthew led us to the towering marble cross on a low hill that dominated the cemetery, then sprinkled holy water on the cross and recited an impressive array of blessings and prayers in both Latin and English. When he was finished, he gently plucked all the petals off the two roses and distributed them among us. "Please toss them at the foot of the cross," he instructed us. "Since Maggie's remains are not available, these petals will have to do as a remembrance of her lovely spirit." He continued to pray as we spread the pink petals over the area he had designated. We started to head back, and just as we passed through the gates Madame Lorraine laid her hand on the priest's shoulder.

"Father, do you think you could please bless this place right here with a little holy water?" She pointed to the spot where I had seen Maggie standing in my dream. How could she have possibly known? But she did. As Father Matthew cast some water on the site, Madame Lorraine and I waved good-bye to the beautiful little ghost as if we could see her. (For all I know, Madame Lorraine did see her.) "Bide in eternal peace, Maggie," she called out.

"You were a wonderful child," I added, still waving. "Good-bye! We love you!" After a few moments of silence we continued our solemn procession.

Back at the church, Father Matthew drew me aside and asked me to join him in his office. Afraid that he was about to deliver a lecture on the indecency of trying to interfere with God's plans for wayward souls, I dragged my feet as I followed him. Once inside his dusty office, he closed the door and gestured for me to have a seat. "Would you like to hear another ghost story?" he said. "A personal one?" Knowing that I would, he didn't wait for my answer, but launched into a tale that helped me understand why he had been so quick to extend his help to a ragtag band of ghostbusters.

"When I was a boy, about eight years old, I was a bit of a wild man," he confided. "My best friend was Jerry Kraus, a ten-year-old who was still in the third grade. Needless to say, he was not the smartest or most hard-working person I've ever known, but he did seem to have a talent for finding trouble. Once he got me to agree to meet him at night in our old barn so we could heat up some Vienna sausages and roast turnips in hot coals. Well, this sounded like the pinnacle of rebellious adventure to a good Catholic boy who nearly always did as his parents told him, so that night I grabbed my flashlight, sneaked out of the house after my parents went to bed, and met Jerry in the barn.

"We were both country boys and we knew that making a fire in a barn held a big risk. That was part of the fun. Nevertheless, we were very careful to clear an area on the floor and make a fire ring out of small stones. Then we added straw and twigs, and Jerry set them alight with a match. He had brought a dozen tiny sausages, which we speared with sticks and held over the flames. All went well for a while, but we soon noticed that fat from the sausages was dripping into the fire, sending sparks into the air. 'We'd better stop,' Jerry said, but by that time it was already too late. One of the sparks had settled onto a bale of dry hay. The hay began smoking, and the next thing we knew the bale was ablaze. If you've ever seen hay on fire, then you know how fast flames can spread through a mountain of straw. By the time we put out our little fire and headed toward the big barn doors, a six-foot-tall sheet of red flames had blocked our way.

"Jerry and I scrambled left and right, searching for a way out, but by then the bone-dry timbers of the barn itself had begun to burn and we were petrified with terror. A rafter, weakened by the fire, fell between us, and I never saw Jerry again. I began to cry. At that moment I heard a voice calling to me above the roar of the fire. A young woman of sixteen or so in a pale blue dress was walking toward me. I was too scared to even wonder how she had gotten into the blazing barn; I just knew I had to follow her. She snatched my hand and dragged me to the back of the barn. The flames parted for us like the Red Sea parted for the Israelites. Then she pushed aside a loose board and shoved me through the opening. We raced away from the burning building just as it burst into a giant yellow fireball.

"The girl in blue still gripped my hand tightly. When I pulled my hand away, I was shocked at what I saw." He held up the stumps of his injured fingers. "It didn't hurt at all, but the sight of those fingers and the thought of losing part of my body frightened me to the core of my being." 'This is so you don't forget,' she told me sternly. 'Don't forget about Jerry and the dangers of starting fires, and don't forget that Providence is watching out for you always.'

"Suddenly my parents were beside me, scolding me and crying at the same time. I looked about for the girl to thank her, but she was gone. When I asked my mom and dad about her, they said my burns had made me was delirious. They meant the injury to my hand, of course, but when they took me to the hospital soon afterwards the doctors were completely stymied. There wasn't one burn mark on my skin, and the stumps had already healed perfectly. The doctors concluded I had been born with this affliction, although my parents insisted that I had not. Only I knew what really happened, but I was certain that none of the grownups would believe me, so I said nothing. You're the first person to hear the real explanation. I usually tell people that I lost the fingers in an accident on the farm. They never press me for details." He stopped, lost in thought for a moment.

"Thank you for being so open with me," I said, genuinely touched by his trust. "Tell me, did your miraculous rescue have anything to do with your decision to enter the priesthood?"

Father Matthew chuckled. "Sort of. Sounds crazy, doesn't it? Other people might have been angry at the Divinity for crippling their hand, but I wasn't. I was glad to be alive, and I thought I must have been spared Jerry's fate for some sort of reason. I wanted to help other people, as the Lord's emissary had helped me, so I just sort of naturally drifted toward the Church. It was almost as if I had a debt to work off. I hope you don't think I'm a few tenors short of a choir."

I smiled and shook his hand. "To a ghostologist, a story like yours sounds perfectly sane." I rose and thanked him for helping us with Maggie. "The poor kid! She never even had her mother's love."

"No," the priest said. "But she has her Father's."

That evening we all dragged ourselves into the sack early. We were drained from our experiences with Maggie and none of us had slept well the night before. I had forgotten we were supposed to meet Esther at the bridge at dawn, but Madame Lorraine and Chelley hadn't forgotten. The sky was still dark when Chelley woke me up from a sound sleep. The rest of the crew was already up, groggy but more or less awake. In contrast, Madame Lorraine was positively energized. "This will be so liberating!" she kept repeating like a mantra as we drove toward the trail. "Imagine! Finally setting a loved one free after 50 years! So liberating!"

I was more in the mood to liberate myself into a nice, fluffy mattress with a big, cozy comforter and a soft pillow, but somehow I kept myself alert enough to guide the car to the head of the trail. Esther's car was already parked in the little lot, and when we pulled in the sun was just beginning to pry open the morning sky. A few rays of gray light seeped over the horizon. I began to catch Madame Lorraine's excitement: something special was about to happen.

We all lent a hand helping Chelley lug her camera equipment down the trail to the first bridge, where old railroad ties lay in a jumble beside the stream. Esther stood on the bridge, leaning on the railing, and waved when she saw us. Something glimmered in her hand, and I soon saw that she held the golden necklace, her father's gift to her, out over the dark water.

Chelley, Tricia and Joe began setting up the camera and recording equipment, and when they were ready they gave me the high sign. Madame Lorraine saw it too. "Esther, are you ready?" she asked. "Are you ready to let go? When you are, just let go."

For a full minute Esther didn't move a muscle. The chain and locket twirled above the water, caught in a gentle morning breeze. Then Esther called out, "I'm ready" and released her grasp on the chain. The necklace sank at once into the water with a golden wink and a tiny gulping noise. "Papa, you're free to go now."

"Are you getting all this?" I whispered to Chelley.

"Yes," she replied, then cried out in wonder, still glued to the camera. "My God! He's here!"

From the corner of my eye I saw a silver shadow glide over the railroad ties. I looked in that direction and beheld a sight I'll never forget. There was George, the Lantern Man, holding his glowing lantern aloft and gazing with a smile into the eyes of his beloved daughter. He was a perfectly normal citizen of Twin Rocks, except that he was transparent, from his rumpled cap to his worn workpants. As we all watched, our gaze fixed on the specter, it began to disintegrate into a sparkling mass of small fragments that swirled and fluttered above the railroad ties like a flock of celestial sparrows. Then the fragments suddenly rose straight up in the air en masse and soon vanished from sight.

"Wow! That's the quickest release I've ever seen!" I whispered to Madame Lorraine, who stood by my side in silent reverence.

She turned to me and smiled. "Well, remember—it was fifty years in the making."

Esther looked upward in the direction her father's spirit had taken and raised her hand in farewell. Tears glinted in her eyes, but her face was lit with the radiance of inner serenity. "Goodbye, Papa," she said. "I love you, and I always will."

THE CRYING ROCK

THE CRYING ROCK

NAMES: *Jenny and Jack Wilderman*

LOCATION: *Large granite rock in middle of Blacklick Creek. Fifty feet from the first bridge on the trail from Twin Rocks to Vintondale.*

LAST MANIFESTATION: *June 17th, 2000*

WARNING: *It is dangerous to attempt to cross the stream.*

This is the story of a sister and brother who got lost in the woods that surround Twin Rocks. This tale resembles stories like Hansel and Gretel, "Babes in the Woods", and other yarns that parents tell their children to deter them from doing something dangerous or going somewhere that may prove unsafe. The difference is, this story is true.

My own parents told me about Jenny and Jack Wilderman when I was very young. It wasn't the normal ghost story like my grandfather told me, with scary descriptions and lots of suspense. They told it more like a news report, answering questions such as who, what, when and where. As I child, I was impressed with their sad story. Then, as childhood memories have a habit of doing, Jack and Jenny slid to the recesses of my mind.

As luck would have it, one day, as I was sifting through the stories and testimonies that people sent me about the ghosts that inhabited the trail, I opened a letter that I had received shortly before leaving Pittsburgh. It was signed simply

"Beatrice" and bore no return address, although it was post-marked Nanty-Glo, Pennsylvania. A small silver medal bearing 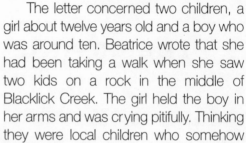 the image of the Virgin Mary slipped out of the envelope and fell onto my lap.

The letter concerned two children, a girl about twelve years old and a boy who was around ten. Beatrice wrote that she had been taking a walk when she saw two kids on a rock in the middle of Blacklick Creek. The girl held the boy in her arms and was crying pitifully. Thinking they were local children who somehow got themselves stranded, Beatrice attempted to help them. As she made her way across the slippery rocks toward the children, she called out to them that everything would be all right. Even so the girl continued to cry. When Beatrice got within a yard of the rock, the children began to fade from sight until they disappeared altogether. When she reached the spot where they had been sitting, Beatrice found nothing but a medal of the Virgin Mary lying on the rock's slick surface.

Beatrice was certain she had encountered two ghosts. When she returned to the bank of the stream, badly shaken, she once again heard the girl crying but was too rattled to look back to see if the children had reappeared. At the end of the letter, Beatrice enclosed directions to the rock where the sighting took place and asked if we'd look into the incident.

Since we were going to be in that area anyway, I decided the tale would make a good story for the book, even though I would not be able to interview first hand the elusive Beatrice. Chelley and I decided to hire a couple of models—Savannah, who was twelve years old, and Max, who was ten—to re-enact the scenario Beatrice had related. We took the children to the very same rock described in the sighting. Although we were careful in guiding the children across the water, Savannah's left foot slipped off a rounded, moss-covered rock and she took a tumble into the shallow water. She was not hurt, only embarrassed.

We threw a crocheted shawl over Savannah's shoulders, then had both kids take off their shoes and sit on the rock. "Lay your lead on Savannah's lap" I told Max, "and pretend you're dead." The idea of playing a corpse appealed to him. Savannah, the grieving sister, whose own death loomed before her, played her part very convincingly.

"Hey, did you bring the medal?" Tricia asked me. "Why not pin it to Savannah's shawl?"

Of course I had brought the medal. I had even sealed it in an envelope to protect it. But when I fished the envelope from my backpack, I was shocked to discover that, although the seal was unbroken, the medal was missing.

"You must have forgotten to put the medal inside," Tricia suggested. "No big deal."

"I guess you're right," I said, although I knew that wasn't the case. I clearly remembered putting the medal in the envelope. Unfortunately, I didn't have any explanation for the medal's sudden disappearance.

The rest of the shoot went without incident. When we finished, Chelley took the film to the local Wal-Mart in Ebensburg for developing. The next day, Joe picked up the photos and met with us on the trail as we searched for the ghost of a local doctor whose incompetence had caused a man's death.

"You are not going to believe this," Joe began, thrusting the packet of photographs into my hand. His face was pasty white, and I could tell from the fright in his eyes that he was not pulling a prank. "You really are not going to believe this. It's just unbelievable."

I opened the package and shuffled through the pictures. "What am I not going to believe?" I asked, examining a photo of Savannah and Max on the Crying Rock.

"Look real close," Joe said. "It's hard to see at first."

I studied the picture carefully. Then it hit me. A feeling of intense cold enveloped me. My skin crawled with the excitement that only the discovery of a real ghost could cause. "I don't believe this," I muttered to myself.

I called Chelley and Tricia over to witness our great success. Behind Savannah and Max stood two other children, barely noticeable: a sickly white, transparent boy and a girl, whose figures I had at first mistaken for water vapor.

Chelley grabbed her magnifying glass and closely examined the photo. "Look here," she said. She pointed to a tiny medal pinned to the ghostly girl's dress. It was identical to the one Beatrice had sent me, the one I had lost.

We were all flying high on our very good luck when things got even more exciting. We were headed back to camp when we neared a road that cut across the trail to a strip-mining operation and saw a frantic man, wearing dirty work clothes, a hard hat and boots, running in our direction.

"Are you the ghost people?" he panted. "Do you have a cell phone?"

We nodded in unison.

"Well, call the police and tell them to get their asses down to the strippings now!"

"What's wrong?" I asked, perplexed by his urgency.

"I found skeletons. Human ones."

We all followed closely behind the man as he ran back to the site. I heard Tricia call the police and give them sketchy details. "We're the ghost people. No, this is not a prank," Tricia yelled into the phone, then covered the mouthpiece and turned toward me. "Is it?" she asked.

I shrugged. "I don't think so. Tell them we'll call them back to confirm. If they don't hear from us in twenty minutes, tell them to show up anyway." No harm in being on the safe side. After all, we were following some wild-eyed stranger into a secluded area.

Still, I had the feeling that the worker, who introduced himself as Terry, was legit. We were only a stone's throw from the place he said he had discovered the remains when the police pulled up.

"How ya doing, Terry?" an officer said, stepping out of his unmarked police car. He put on his blue cap and walked toward me. "She causing you trouble?" he asked Terry, as he pointed his finger at me. "What do you say I cuff her and take her in?"

"You're a real jerk," I said as he grabbed my hands and held them together. Terry and my crew all gasped at the sight of me being "arrested."

"Ghostbusting is illegal in these parts," he stated, in a deep, monotonal, policeman-like voice. "I was hoping I wouldn't have to arrest you, you being my cousin and all."

We both laughed and gave each other a big hug.

"How've you been, Squirt?" he asked. "I heard you've become a big-time ghost investigator. You actually make a living doing that, or does your old man pay your way?"

"Speaking of spouses," I answered, "how's that lovely wife of yours?" Then I corrected myself. "Oh that's right, she left you, didn't she?"

We were about to throw a few more of our standard, nasty remarks at each other when Terry grabbed my hand and turned me toward him.

"Please! Hurry! There's two of 'em. They're over there." He pointed to a heap of dirt at the edge of the woods. "Follow me." As we made our way across the bumpy terrain, Terry explained

that he was removing the topsoil when a tree limb got stuck in his blade. As he got out to remove it, something caught his leg and he stumbled, falling right onto the final resting place of the two unknowns.

"Any idea who they could be?" Terry asked, bending down to brush away some of the dirt from the bones. "I'll be you dollars to donuts that it's the Wilderman kids."

"Wait!" I shouted, catching sight of a metal object attached to a fragment of cloth. I took a closer look. "Chelley, come and take a picture of this."

"What is it?" she asked.

"It's a medal of the Virgin Mary."

It has only been a few months since Terry uncovered the bones. Preliminary results show that they are the skeletal remains of two children—a girl and a boy, twelve and ten years old respectively. They are believed to be Jenny and Jack Wilderman, lost in the forest in the fall of 1945. Sadly, they were less than half a mile from their home when they died. The coroner speculated that their deaths might have been caused by hypothermia, but there was no way to tell for sure. Why they could not find their way back home is a matter for Madame Lorraine, who has yet been unable to communicate with the children, whose bones have received a proper burial.

At the time of this printing, no further sightings of the children have been reported.

MADAME LORRAINE'S COMMENT:
Now that the children are at rest in hallowed ground, their souls, like Maggie's, should be released. However, as it is not unusual for a spirit's voice to linger behind its image, alert people may still hear the voice of a child crying by the stream, although no children can be seen. This is no cause for alarm.

ELIZA'S FURNACE

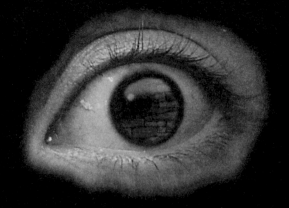

ELIZA'S FURNACE

NAME: *Mikhail Eliza*

LOCATION: *Eliza's Furnace, Vintondale*

MANIFESTATIONS: *Reports of sightings are documented as far back as 1860. Most recent sighting June 21, 2000. Random. Most manifestations take the form of a distraught man with red, blistered skin and severe burns. According to reports, he has spoken only once.*

WARNING: *Do not remove the protective grates from the openings in the furnace. Never attempt to enter the furnace.*

I learned of Mikhail Eliza's ghost, along with 30 other kids, when I was in the fourth grade. Miss Deckerman, our teacher, a nice but rather lonely woman, decided that, instead of having the traditional class picnic at Duman's Dam, we would walk to Eliza's Furnace and learn some local history. So, following her instructions, we all gathered at the playground behind the school, twenty minutes before the first bell on Friday before the last week of school. All of us dutifully brought a bag lunch and a bottle of water, and wore sensible walking shoes, just as Miss Deckerman had insisted. Miss Deckerman was already there, looking competent in a woodsy sort of way in a khaki pantsuit and a wide-brimmed straw hat.

The plan, as Miss Deckerman explained to us, was to enter the woods adjacent to the schoolyard, follow the narrow path single-file for one mile, then follow the pipeline clearing for another two miles. Then we would walk two by two on yet

another path for one mile that would lead us to Eliza's Furnace, where we could break for lunch and play tag and duck-duck-goose before heading back. She promised us a "special treat" if we were good.

"Stay together," she warned us, waving her forefinger at us sternly. "You never know what's out there." And we really didn't. Each and every one of us was concerned about Miss Deckerman's decision to enter "those" woods. We all knew the story about Petey Bagley, a sixth grader, who disobeyed the most important playground rule: Never leave the playground and go into the woods. He left the school at recess and never came back. They said he was last seen going into the very same woods that Miss Deckerman was about to enter with almost three dozen nervous nine-year-olds. Petey Bagley aside, it was common knowledge that Miss Deckerman had what our parents politely termed "a drinking problem".

"Everyone ready," Miss Deckerman barked, shepherding us into a long line. "No chattering."

"Miss Deckerman, Miss Deckerman!" Larry Pilette thrust his hand high in the air. "What about Petey Bagley?"

"What about him?" She offered a tissue to Susie Leeber, whose nose was running like a faucet.

"Will we see him?"

"Why would we possibly see him?" Miss Deckerman asked, snatching John Wilker's verbotten transistor radio from his hands while still looking at Larry. I never understood how she could do that.

"I mean, will we see his ghost?" The entire class gasped in chorus, then fell dead silent.

"There's no such thing as ghosts," Miss Deckerman sniffed. "Besides, Petey isn't dead. He moved to another town."

"Which one?" Larry persisted.

"I don't remember. It isn't important. Now stop that non-sense before you scare everyone."

Everyone was already scared. We all knew what the adults said about Petey Bagley: He moved. Sometimes they said to Belsano, sometimes to Johnstown. Sometimes, as Miss Deckerman had said, to parts unknown. But we kids knew better. Petey Bagley died somewhere in those woods.

When everyone was in line, Miss Deckerman inspected us with military precision. "Larry," she commanded, "keep to the back of the line and make sure we don't lose anyone."

"But, Miss...."

"Go," she said, with an imperious flourish of her hand. I wasn't sure if Miss Deckerman picked Larry to act as rear guard as some sort of punishment for bringing up Petey Bagley or because he was the tallest, strongest boy in the fourth grade. All I knew for sure was that he was scared. After all, who would be protecting his backside?

As he walked past us, we all reached out and touched him, as if he were a dead man walking. I will always respect him for holding his head high, with an air of doomed dignity. It was at that moment I chose him to be my new boyfriend. All I had to do was tell my old boyfriend, Vince Parcelli, that he wasn't my boyfriend any more and tell Larry that he was. I figured the sooner everyone knew where they stood, the better.

I watched my classmates disappear one by one into the dark shadows of the woods. Finally, it was my turn. I plunged into the cool darkness, eyes half closed, more than a little anxious. Still, I felt somewhat comforted knowing that Larry was protecting our rear.

After half an hour or so we all calmed down and began to chatter about the things that nine-year- olds chatter about. Petey Bagley's ghost was the last thing on our minds. I had exchanged places with the kids in front of me until I was walking behind Vince.

"Hey," I whispered, "I don't want to be your girlfriend anymore, okay?"

"Okay," he agreed. "You want your pencil back?"

"You keep it." Although it was my favorite pencil, bright red with a green foil number eight printed on it, I wanted him to have something to remember me by.

"Thanks," he said. "I think I'm going to ask Linda Johnson to be my girlfriend."

By noon we reached Eliza's Furnace and gathered around it to listen patiently as Miss Deckerman gave us a short history lesson. Eliza's Furnace was one of the best-preserved hot blast furnaces in the state and operated from 1846 to 1849, when it was closed following a tragic accident. I didn't pay much attention to the lecture; the furnace looked more like an Aztec pyramid than a furnace to me. I didn't get the point of the whole thing. But I did notice Vince smiling at Linda Johnson, whose boyfriend, Stanley Stanish, was standing right beside him. Poor Vince! I thought for sure he was going to get beaten up.

"Wasn't that fascinating?" Miss Deckerman asked.

"Yes, Miss Deckerman," we chanted. Finally, she dismissed us with a wave of her hand. We were free to eat our lunch and play.

Betty Jo Sherman and I exchanged sandwiches. I was halfway through two thick slices of wheat bread slathered with homemade strawberry jelly when Betty Jo prodded me in the ribs. "Look ," she said, pointing at a cluster of kids. "Your boyfriend is talking to that ugly Linda Johnson. I don't know why Stanley likes her. He's so cute."

"Vince isn't my boyfriend anymore," I informed her. "We broke up this morning. I like Larry now."

Betty Jo and I saw Larry at the same time, climbing up the wall of the furnace, as strong and agile as a leopard. And so handsome! His blond hair was a few shades lighter than mine and he was almost as tall as me. We had so much in common that I was surprised we didn't like each other before this. "I'm going to tell him that he's my new boyfriend," I decided aloud.

"Go on, go on," Betty Jo encouraged me.

I headed toward the furnace and watched Larry climb to the top. "Way to go!" I called up to him, clapping my hands shamelessly.

He smiled and waved at me, then began climbing back down. He jumped off the furnace when he was half way down and landed on his feet. Then he lost his balance and fell to one side. "That was a great jump," I said, helping him up. "Would like you to be my boyfriend?" I asked, not wasting any time.

"Sure," he answered, without a second thought. "Here, you can have my penknife." He reached into his pocket and handed me an inch-long green plastic penknife bearing the inscription, *Burko's Auto Mart*.

"Wait here. I have something for you," I said, running off toward my jacket, which lay in a crumpled heap next to Betty Jo. I thought my keychain from Storybook Forest would be a great going-steady gift.

Then it happened.

Just as I was searching my jacket for the keychain, Larry started screaming at the top of his lungs. Everyone came running, including Miss Deckerman. Larry stood in the archway of the west opening of the furnace, screaming and pointing at something. "H…help!" he stuttered. "He's on fire! He's on fire!"

Miss Deckerman pulled him out of the opening and tried to calm him down, but he began screaming, "Eliza's burning!"

The rest of us started to run in every direction like panicked sheep, screaming in terror as if we were about to be massacred. The people who lived across the street hurried over to help Miss Deckerman round us up and calm us down. Finally they got us settled, and, as a local woman fed us chocolate chip cookies, we watched Larry being carried to a big black car and placed lying down in the back seat. I cried as I watched them drive Larry, my former new boyfriend, away.

"Is he dead?" I asked Miss Deckerman as we stood waiting for the arrival of the school bus to take us home.

"No." She carefully opened a blue plastic thermos and poured herself a cup of dark liquid that smelled like coffee mixed with cough syrup. "He's scared. He thinks he saw the ghost of Mikhail Eliza."

"Mick…who?"

"The man who died a long time ago in the furnace. Remember the story I told you this morning? The furnace was named after him. His name was originally Elitchka, but over the years people starting saying Eliza."

I shook my head and vowed to listen more closely the next time anyone explained the history of mysterious furnaces.

"No one's sure what happened," Miss Deckerman explained. "They didn't keep very good records back in 1849, but they think Eliza went back late at night to fix a loose stone at the top of the furnace and must have fallen in the fire."

"And?"

"And what? End of story. Now how about you helping me get everyone lined up? The bus should be here any minute."

We all made it home safely. The next day at school I searched for Larry but he wasn't there. We only had a week of school left before summer vacation and his parents decided to keep him home. I didn't see him again until we started the fifth grade. By then the whole Eliza incident was forgotten. I had a new boyfriend and Miss Deckerman decided to take her new fourth grade students to Duman's Dam.

While I was working on this book, I recalled the incidents of that day at Eliza's Furnace. I tracked down Larry and gave him a call. He was living in San Francisco, happily married, with two beautiful children and a rewarding career as a partner in a very successful law firm. He was genuinely happy to hear from me. We joked about us being boyfriend and girlfriend for a day.

"I know why you're calling," he said, getting straight to the point. "You want to know what happened that day at Eliza's Furnace."

"Yes," I answered, not surprised that he may have heard I was gathering information about the hauntings. Twin Rocks was a small town, and talk spread far and wide. "Who told you?"

"Betty Jo Sherman. Well, now she's Betty Jo Sherman-Hoffsburger. She said you interviewed her about some kid, I forget his name. The one that was electrocuted. She said you would probably get around to remembering Eliza."

"So...? Are you going to tell me what happened?"

There was a long, loud silence. This was not unusual coming from Larry. On and off throughout the years I had asked him what happened when he encountered the spirit of Eliza, but he refused to talk about the incident.

"Larry...." I lowered my voice. "It's time to let it go." Again more silence, followed by a long sigh.

"Okay, you're the doctor," he said, his tone much lighter now. "We had just decided to go steady. I gave you my green penknife and you ran off. I watched you fumbling through your pockets, searching for something."

"A keychain from Storybook Forest," I said. "I still have it, next to your knife in a box in my attic."

He laughed, then became serious again. "After you left, I thought I heard someone call my name and I went through the archway. I felt chills run up and down my entire body, and as I neared the center of the furnace, a voice whispered to me, softly, as if the words were carried on a breeze. 'Jimmy... Jimmy O'Brien?'

"I was going to run but I thought that one of the guys was playing a trick on me since I had made such a big deal out of Petey Bagley. I didn't want to look like a coward in front of you, so I played along.

"'I'm not Jimmy O'Brien,' I said.

"'You were Jimmy O'Brien.'

"'I was never Jimmy O'Brien. I've always been Larry Pilette.'

"'Not so!' The voice grew louder. 'You were once my trusted friend, the best man at my wedding. How could you have done this to me?'

"I was beginning to get a little scared, but I decided to keep humoring whoever it was. 'So what did I do to you?' I asked.

"Then the voice said, 'You threw me into the flames so you could marry my sweet, lovely wife.'

"'Katrina?' I said, but even as I said the name I didn't know how I could possibly have known it.

"'Yes, my Katrina. And now Jimmy, my old friend and murderer and husband of my wife...you must prepare to die.'

"That's when I saw flames. I know no one else saw them, but they sure felt real to me. I started to burn. My arms and legs were on fire. I could feel the fire and smell my flesh burning. I wasn't imagining anything. I knew I was burning. I started screaming. Then I saw him staring at me. It had to be Mikhail Eliza. His skin was burned bright red and terror glowed in his eyes. I could feel his wrenching pain. The next thing I knew Miss Deckerman was pulling me out of the furnace and you were staring at me as if you'd seen a ghost.

"Weird, isn't it? But it gets better. I did a lot of research on Eliza and this Jimmy O'Brien. It seems that I'm a distant cousin of ol' Jimmy, related on his mother's side. In fact I have a wedding picture of Jimmy and Katrina that I found in the attic after my mother died. It seems that Jimmy married Katrina shortly after Mikhail's 'accident' in the furnace. She had three kids to raise but no money, so she didn't have much of a choice."

I thought silently for a moment. "Do you think she suspected that Jimmy was a murderer?"

"Oh, I know she knew. She used to visit the furnace every evening in the summer. Her neighbors used to hear her singing Mikhail's favorite hymn, as if trying to comfort him, and they knew how deeply she'd been hurt by Mikhail's death. When she died, she was found holding Mikhail's death card—you know, the kind people used to give out at funerals long ago. She was also holding a piece of paper with her written confession. She wrote that she always had a feeling that Jimmy killed Mikhail because he could never mention Mikhail's name without getting very upset. At first she thought it was because he missed Mikhail so much. But then Jimmy started drinking and she could read the guilt in his eyes. On his deathbed he finally admitted his crime to Katrina and asked forgiveness. According to her, she forgave him in hopes that Mikhail Eliza's restless spirit would one day find a way to forgive Jimmy, so he could move on to heaven where she would be waiting for him."

By now I was pretty excited about the prospects of seeing Eliza for myself and helping to set him free. I'm sure Larry could hear the eagerness in my voice when I asked him, "How do we get Eliza to pass over?"

"I don't know," Larry answered. I imagined a smile playing on his lips. "I'm leaving it up to you professional ghost hunters. I'm sure you'll find a way."

MADAME LORRAINE'S SUGGESTION: *Obviously, Mikhail Eliza is still very angry over being brutally ripped away from his beloved wife by a false friend. To help soothe his soul and prepare him for release, sing or recite a line of your favorite hymn or other old, melodic song. This may help soothe his rage and turn his mind to thoughts of forgiveness.*

SHEILA
REMEMBERED

SHEILA REMEMBERED

NAME: *Sheila Reicher*

LOCATION: *The softly sloping hillside called Sheep Hill, near the Pipeline. Now seen on the Ghost Town Trail near the town of Vintondale.*

MANIFESTATIONS: *Fairly often. First documented sighting occurred on May 20, 1986. Most recent sighting: April 13, 2000. Appears as a girl on horseback. Never reported to be on foot. Auditory manifestations include hoofbeats, a girl's voice, and/or a horse's neigh. Most often seen or heard early in the morning or near twilight.*

Sheila Reicher and I went to school together, but I didn't know her very well. She was a year older than me and traveled in a different crowd. I didn't think much about her until eighth grade, when I returned from a long visit with relatives to find out that Sheila had died a week after I'd left on my trip. It was the autumn of 1971. The Vietnam War had ended, and for most of us, life was good. For the Reicher family, it was a nightmare.

The Reichers were some of the most popular people in Twin Rocks. They lived on what we called a "gentleman's farm," that is, a few acres of land with a big garden, some chickens, and a small stable that housed the two horses belonging to Sheila and her younger sister, Katie. The sisters, each of whom had brilliant red hair that shone like a bonfire, absolutely adored each other. You almost never saw one without the other, and

To Everyone:

My name is Sheila Lynn Reicher and I'm very happy to be alive. I'm almost 13 years old, live on a farm, and I have a sister named Katy and a horse named Rowdy. I love my family very much and they love me, too. Someday, I would like to be a ballerina. Even if I don't, I'll still be happy. I have a boyfriend, Louie Dunston. He's the cutest boy in school, and maybe someday we'll get married. We'll have two daughters who I'll teach to ride a horse and dance. But my favorite times are with Rowdy. Riding him is my most favorite thing in the world. I like it more than opening gifts on Christmas Day. He understands how I feel and I never have to say a word. I'm free as the wind when I'm riding him because my little spur, Rowdy, is like the wind. It's a strange way we belong to each other. I know what is on his mind and he knows what is on mine. One day, when we die, we will both ride the wind.

Sheila

you almost never saw Sheila when she wasn't talking a mile a minute about her Appaloosa horse, Rowdy.

I always assumed that Sheila had crossed over peacefully. Her death was sudden, but her life had been almost idyllic, marred only with the usual moments of teenage instability. But when I'd heard that visitors to the trail had been glimpsing the image of a red-haired girl on a spotted horse, I knew that Sheila was either not resting as comfortably as I thought, or was just plain reluctant to leave the world.

Since the start of our investigation, I had pored over newspaper accounts of Sheila's accident and interviews with her parents, friends and teachers, but I was never able to get a clear picture of her story. When a cashier at the Gold Crown Foodland in Nanty-Glo told me that Sheila's sister Katie still lived in Twin Rocks, I thought she just might be able to help me.

Katie agreed to meet me for breakfast at the Corner Restaurant. She was a pretty woman, like her sister, with soft brown eyes and a complexion that still looked like peaches and cream. I could sense that Katie had some hidden feelings about her sister, and I decided not to push her into any embarrassing revelations. After a slow, awkward start, our conversation began to heat up a little when I mentioned Rowdy. "Whatever happened to that horse, anyway?" I asked.

"Oh, he died a while ago," Katie said, spreading apple butter on her wheat toast. "He was really old, about 30, which is over 90 in human years. Gosh, but Sheila loved to ride that Appy."

"How about you?" I said. I wanted to talk about Sheila, but I also wanted to make sure that Katie felt comfortable first. "You liked riding too, didn't you?"

"Sort of, but I never enjoyed it as much as her. Sheila, she just took to it naturally. You ever see her and Rowdy gallop across Sheep Hill like wild things?" I shook my head. "Well, you should have. She looked so pretty, her hair blowing straight back behind her like a flame." Katie paused to run her hand across her eyes. "I'm sorry, but even now it's not easy to talk about that night."

I gently encouraged Katie to tell me what happened. To help her remember, I showed her a copy of an article from the *Vintondale Times*, published right after the incident on May 1.

The *Times* article was short and straightforward. It recounted how Sheila, playing in a field near the house, had fallen into an abandoned well and become caught in the deep, narrow channel. Rescue attempts failed, and Sheila suffocated only hours after becoming trapped. There was a brief description of Sheila's accomplishments in school and a paragraph giving funeral information.

Katie picked up the article, glanced at it and tossed it on the table in front of her, frowning. "That thing made me mad," she said, tugging on a lock of her own fiery red hair, now streaked with pale gold. "It's not that the story is wrong, exactly, but it left out the most important detail. See, Sheila wasn't playing in the field. I was, and she was looking after me. We both knew about the well, which was covered up with boards, but I was young, stupid and headstrong. I loved to tease Sheila by standing on the boards and daring her to chase me off. Once while I was doing that, the boards began to crack and give way under my weight. I screamed, and Sheila came running up to me. She pushed me off onto the ground just before the boards broke, but by the time I got up and started looking for her, she was gone. She had fallen into the well instead of me." Katie blotted her face with an apple-butter-stained paper napkin. "She saved me, only to die instead of me."

I reached across the table and patted her shoulder in what I hoped was a reassuring manner. "It wasn't your fault that she died, you know," I said. "You're not still beating up on yourself, are you?"

Katie shook her head and brushed her bangs her face. "No," she sniffed, and took a deep breath. When she continued her voice was normal. "I was a kid, a foolish kid. No one can blame a kid. But I'll tell you this, not a day goes by but I think of my sister in that well and my heart breaks all over again." Katie paused and swallowed hard.

As I sat in the restaurant, consoling Katie, a memory I had pushed to the back of my mind suddenly pushed its way into my consciousness. Although I hadn't really recognized it until that moment, Sheila Reicher had had a huge affect on me, but only after she had been dead for a year.

At the beginning of eighth grade, Mrs. Engstrom, the principal, asked me to stay after school and sort all the various textbooks, to make sure they were free of papers, pencil marks, and dog-eared edges. I'm sure she meant this task as a punishment of some sort, but I can't remember what I did to deserve it. All I knew was that it was a glorious autumn afternoon and I wanted to be with my friends, hanging out at the drugstore, not arranging dusty books for kids I had no interest in.

I spent the next hour sorting books into neat stacks of English, Math, Social Studies and Science. When I picked up one especially worn English book, a sheet of notebook paper sailed out from its pages like a bird. It was a letter, written in the large, looping handwriting of a young girl.

I began to read it, and soon I was enveloped in a dead girl's love of living.

"To Everyone," it began. "My name is Sheila Lynn Reicher and I'm very happy to be alive. I'm almost thirteen years old, live on a farm and I have a sister named Katy and a horse named Rowdy. I love my family very much and they love me, too." I recalled how my hands trembled as I read about her wanting to be a ballerina. It was a sad and moving experience to read about the dreams and hopes of someone who had passed over. I felt a little frightened in a small way because it seemed to me as though Sheila were talking to me from the grave. I began to cry at the part where Sheila wrote that she was hoping to marry her steady boyfriend, Louie Dinston, after high school. "We'll have two daughters who I'll teach to ride a horse and to dance." But, the part of the letter that touched me the most was about Rowdy. Maybe it was because of my own love for my black Labrador Retriever, Dutchman.

"Riding him is my most favorite thing in the world. I like it more than opening gifts on Christmas day. He understands how I'm feeling and I never have to say a word. I'm free as the wind when I'm riding him because my little sugar, Rowdy, is like the wind. In a strange sort of way, we belong to each other. I know what is on his mind and he knows what is on mine. One day, when we both die we will ride on the wind.

The letter ended with a drawing of a happy face, its eyes closed in delight and its U-shaped mouth taking up the entire lower half of its face. Beside it was a sketch of a horse with a big, silly grin. Underneath the picture, Sheila wrote in dark, block letters, "Life is wonderful when you're riding a horse."

I sat in the school desk, completely stunned. Had Sheila known—on some strange level, in some inexplicable way—that her happy life was soon to come to an end? There was no way of knowing for certain, but one thing was clear: Sheila Reicher had been living her life to the fullest every chance she got.

Suddenly I was back in the coffee shop in Twin Rocks, sitting across from Katie and remembering with a shock that I still had Sheila's letter.

I had to be sure, however, before I mentioned anything to Katie. After we parted, I hurried back to camp where I began a frantic search through my private files. Finally I unearthed Sheila's letter, stuffed in a faded pink envelope and filed under "Big Bend Grade School." I had kept it all those years to remind me that life is short, and we must make the most of life every day, for that day could be our last. Although I had temporarily forgotten that message, the Fates had conspired to make me remember it.

In the course of writing this book, I saw Katie again, this time in the living room of her home in Vintondale, where I gave her Sheila's letter. As she read it, tears of joy and pride streamed down her face, nearly obscuring her smile. "Yes, that's my sister," she said softly, laying the paper on the table in front of her. "I never knew a happier soul. She was just so full of the joy of living."

I leaned forward, acting on a hunch. "Katie, I don't mean to disturb you, but did you happen to…see Sheila again? After the accident?"

Katie looked up at me. Her lips curved upward in a faint, haunting smile. "You mean her ghost, right?"

"Well…." I grinned helplessly. "Yes. If you did, don't worry. I won't think you're crazy."

Katie began toying with the corner of the letter. "Okay, it was like this. After Sheila died, I took care of Rowdy, and I was proud to do so. As long as I was around him, I felt that Sheila was still alive. It was like she talked to me through that horse.

"Rowdy had a happy life. When he got sick that last time, I stayed all night in the barn with him, trying to comfort him. He wasn't in pain, he just couldn't get up, which is very distressing to a horse."

I recalled some accounts I'd read about animals perceiving spirits that were invisible to humans. "Did he exhibit any unusual behavior?" I asked.

"In a way," Katie answered. "It was three in the morning. There wasn't a sound inside or out, but suddenly Rowdy raised his head and pricked his ears forward, like he did whenever Sheila entered the barn. I looked where he was looking, but I couldn't see anything. When I looked back at Rowdy, he had passed away. I swear, if horses could smile, there was a smile on the face of that old guy. Right at that moment, my arms began to shiver. I heard what I thought was the sound of the wind and from the corner of my eye I saw two shadows streak through the door. I didn't believe in ghosts until that very moment."

Katie was the first to see her sister's ghost, but there have been numerous sightings since then, most in the Sheep Hill area near the Pipeline. Lately, however, manifestations have been occurring all along the length of the Ghost Town Trail. People say they've seen a girl with red hair riding a white horse with black spots across the trail, and suddenly horse and rider just aren't there anymore. Some manifestations are as subtle as a flash of red and white and the smell of leather. Other people have heard the neigh of a horse and the laughter of a young woman, barely audible over the thunder of hoofbeats on still, hot summer evenings. Still others, in the quiet of the early morning, have heard a whisper on the breeze: "Go, sugar, like the wind." Most recently, visitors to the trail have reported hearing the sound of horse hooves clip-clopping behind them, but when they turn to look, there's no horse.

Doctor J. S. Rickovich, who agreed to be interviewed for this book, told us that he had both heard and seen the phantom horse and rider. "I was walking the trail around 5:00 o'clock on a Thursday afternoon, April 13, 2000. I wrote it all down in my journal," he said, handing me a black notebook. "Anyway, as I said, it was around five and I was entering a marshy area near where they are building the new park. That was when I saw this beautiful black and white horse standing in the middle of the marsh. At first I panicked, thinking that the animal was stuck in the mud. Suddenly, I heard a girl's voice. It sounded like she said something about the wind. Then, right before my eyes, a girl, I'd say about thirteen or so, with long red hair and cream-colored skin, was sitting on the back of the horse. She waved at me and then they both disappeared."

"What do you mean, 'disappeared'?" I asked, jotting down his testimony, as I often do to reinforce taped interviews.

"They vanished," he said, in an awestruck voice.

"You mean that the girl rode the horse into the woods?"

"No." He shook his head slowly to emphasize his answer. "They didn't move. They just…dissolved. I know it sounds insane, but that's what happened."

I assured him that I didn't think he was insane.

MADAME LORRAINE'S SUGGESTION: *This young girl is happy in the land of shadows, but she will ultimately be happier once she fully accepts her death. To help her make a comfortable transition out of the land of the living, set something sweet on the trail, like a piece of candy, a few cookie crumbs or drops of soft drink. In this way, she will know that she has been remembered and that we, the living, agree with her that life is a sweet treasure, sometimes all too easily crushed. And horse-lovers, don't worry: Wherever Sheila goes, she'll be riding Rowdy.*

MIS-DIE-AGNOSED

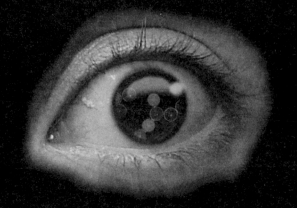

MIS-DIE-AGNOSED

NAME: *Dr. Quentin Itherman*

LOCATION: *Anywhere along the stretch of trail from Nanty-Glo to Dilltown.*

MANIFESTATION: *People have encountered small whirlwinds of dust and debris along the trail, even when there is no wind at all, not even a puff. Very rarely this ghost manifests in human form, most often as the faint image of a man smoking a cigar and sweeping in front of himself with a broom. This manifestation lingers only a moment or two, but you should at least be able to glimpse a frowning face and catch a whiff of tobacco smoke.*

Around twelve-thirty one afternoon, we stopped for lunch near mile marker four. Our lunch-time menu was definitely European—crusty bread, cheese and red wine. After we finished our meal, Joe gathered up the trash. As he was placing it into a small plastic garbage bag, he accidentally dropped the cork to the wine bottle.

Suddenly, out of nowhere a small whirlwind of dust swept by like a miniature tornado on a mission, picked up the cork, then vanished, cork and all, as quickly as it had come.

"What was that?" Joe asked. A bewildered and, I must say, frightened look crossed his face.

"My guess is that Doc was making an appearance," I replied.

"Is Doc a ghost?" Chelley asked, emptying the last drops of wine from her glass on the trail. "For Sheila and Rowdy," she said, following Madame Lorraine's suggestion.

"As a matter of fact, he is," I said. "Would you like to hear his story? It will only take a few minutes," I promised, knowing that my storytelling could sometimes get out of hand.

"Sure, why not?" Tricia glanced at her watch. "We have a half-hour before we're supposed to meet up with Madame Lorraine."

Before starting the story, I briefly recalled my own career in the medical field. I had discovered first-hand that medicine is not an exact science by witnessing doctors who tried to separate the illness from the patient, only to sometimes end up separating the patient from his earthly existence. This proves that doctors are not gods. Or are they? After all, they have the power of life and death, don't they? One simple misdiagnosis can cause a warm body full of life to turn stone cold dead.

We started walking down the trail, pushing our bikes toward Twin Rocks.

"Melvin 'Candy Mel' Millhouse was the father of my friend Trudie," I began. "Melvin's nickname was derived from his initials, an M and another M. He was a nice guy, but what happened to him shouldn't have happened to anyone. Keep in mind that this incident took place in a time before HMOs, rampant malpractice suits and the patient's bill of rights. It was also a time when a rural doctor might prescribe chewing on a sprig of mint to relieve an upset stomach, and treat constipation by suggesting the sufferer eat an apple, followed by a chocolate bar. Unfortunately for Candy Mel, in those days information on

the latest medical breakthroughs was not accessible to the 'common man.' Therefore, it didn't occur to anyone to question the soundness of a doctor's treatments, and seeking a second opinion was simply unheard of.

"Candy Mel was a humble man of very moderate means. He never owned a car and rented a modest, two-bedroom bungalow that housed him, his wife and five children. He only had two known vices—gambling, and an obsessive urge to constantly munch on the small, colorful, candy-coated chocolates that bore his initials. He was more than generous in sharing this treat with anyone who seemed to need a bit of instant happiness.

"Candy Mel's presence was virtually part of the town of Twin Rocks. He could be seen hitching a ride to work, walking to church with his family, or carrying home a load of groceries. The townsfolk were always slipping Candy Mel a dollar or two, loading him up with presents for Trudie and the other kids at Christmas time, and occasionally paying off the debts he incurred during the weekly poker game held in the basement of Mr. Weazel's house. He would always repay the kindness others showed to him and his family by trimming hedges, shoveling snow off steps and sidewalks and performing other helpful tasks. One way or another, Candy Mel always paid his way.

"One day Candy Mel, unable to hitch a ride home from his night job at the steel mills, walked the seventeen miles from Johnstown to Twin Rocks. When he reached the outskirts of town, he began to experience shortness of breath, an upset stomach, numbness in his jaw, and a dull, aching pain that radiated from his chest all the way down his left arm. Thinking he was coming down with the flu, he made his way to the office of Dr. Quentin Itherman and stumbled into the examining room, where he was greeted by the noxious aroma of the good doctor's fat Cuban cigar.

"My sister used to hate the smell of his cigars." I interrupted my own story to relate a brief episode from my childhood, when my sister was six and I was ten years old. "She told him straight out, 'Your cigar is stinky.' That's when he jabbed her in the foot with a needle, supposedly in an effort to remove a splinter.

"That hurts!" she screamed into Dr. Itherman's ear.

"Aw, no, it doesn't," he snarled at her. "Stay still or I'll give you a poke with one of these." He gestured toward a metal tray full of large syringes.

But my sister wasn't finished. "How do you know it doesn't hurt? It's my foot," she yelled. "How would like me to stick you with one of those needles?"

Joe waved his hand in the air. Though he had come to know me very well over the years, he did not have much patience with my digressions. "Cute, but please get back to your story. I want to hear about that whirlwind."

"Okay," I relented, though the story about my sister could easily have gone on for another hour. "So...after listening to Candy Mel relate his symptoms, the doctor gave him a brief examination, consisting chiefly of a thoughtful 'hmmm' and a few pokes to the stomach. 'Constipation,' Dr. Itherman said flatly, blowing smoke in Candy Mel's face. 'When was the last time you moved your bowels?'

Candy Mel couldn't remember.

"'You need to poop,' the doctor concluded. 'All that chocolate is binding you up.' With that brilliant diagnosis, Dr. Itherman mixed up a triple dose of milk of magnesia fortified with cod liver oil and horehound extract, then handed it to Candy Mel, who gulped it down without question. If he had known that Dr. Itherman's medical license had almost been revoked—once in Ohio, once in Pennsylvania—he might have not been so quick to accept the doc's 'cure'.

"'Ten bucks,' the doctor said, stretching out his hand. 'Cash on the ol' barrelhead.' He smiled grimly, exposing a dark brown tobacco stain that ringed the inside of his lips.

"Candy Mel counted out six one-dollar bills and two dollars in change and handed it all over. "Can I pay the rest in chocolate?" he asked, grimacing in pain. 'I've got a brand-new bag at home.'

"'Never eat the stuff. Rots your teeth,' Dr. Itherman answered, sucking on his stogie. 'You can work off your debt. How about burying those needles in the woods for me?' He pointed to a cardboard box filled to the brim with used and broken needles. 'Can't throw them in the trash ever since that Eberly boy fished one out and stuck himself with it. Wish the school weren't next door.'

"Candy Mel, by now barely able to stand, was eager to please. He made his way across the room, slowly picked up the box and shuffled out the door of the office.

"'Trowel's in the garage," Dr. Itherman called after him. 'Be careful to dig at least a foot down. Don't want anybody to find them. And for God's sake, hurry home afterwards.'

"The rest of the day passed normally for Dr. Itherman. When evening came he decided to make sure that Candy Mel had completed his chore. What if the big brute had simply left the box in the woods, he thought, or worse yet, dumped the needles out on the ground and left them exposed?

"The doctor followed a faint trail into the woods behind his house. When he came across Candy Mel's body sprawled on the path, surrounded by syringes, he only had one thing to say. 'Damn it! Now I have to bury the stuff myself.'

"A brief investigation determined that Candy Mel died of a massive heart attack. There was never even a suggestion of negligence on the part of his physician. Dr. Itherman continued to practice his brand of medicine without incident for several years after Candy Mel's death. Then one night in his sleep, the good doctor simply shuffled off his mortal coil. But he didn't get too far.

"Now Candy Mel, a victim of incompetent treatment from an uncaring doctor, seems to be at peace. Not one single manifestation of his spirit has ever been reported. However, interestingly enough, Dr. Itherman's spirit has been spotted on the trail. It seems as if a power wiser and more just than human law has ruled that the doctor must pay his worldly debts before moving on. He seems to have become the trail's custodian, working for his victim and humanity in general. His job is to sweep the trail from dusk to dawn, cleaning the way for visitors. So, should you see a cloud of dust whirl across the Ghost Town Trail, it isn't the wind at work. It's Dr. Janitor."

"Not a bad story," Chelley said.

"It was okay," Joe commented. "But I don't think it was one of your best."

"Oh?" I tried hard to hide my indignation. I usually take criticism pretty well, but I wasn't in the mood for it that day. Then I remembered the snack I had brought with me from camp.

We all walked on quietly for a few minutes, and I made sure to fall behind the others a little. Suddenly I shrieked as loudly as I could and let my bicycle fall to the ground.

"What's the matter?" Joe dropped his bike and rushed to my side.

I quickly pulled a packet of Candy Mel's favorite chocolates from the pocket of my jeans jacket and held the bag up in front of Joe. He stopped in his tracks. "Oh, no!" I cried, shaking the bag to make the candies rattle like a timber rattler's tail. "It's the deadly chocolates from Hell! They've come to get Joe!"

Joe wasn't impressed, and he certainly wasn't scared. "Gimme those!" He grabbed the packet from my hand, ripping it in the process. Red, blue, green, yellow and brown candies flew through the air and scattered all over the trail. "I wish you wouldn't do things like that," he said, staring at the unintended decorations.

"Should we clean them up?" Tricia asked.

"No, leave them for Sheila and Rowdy," Chelley answered. We all agreed.

We had just resumed our trek up the trail when Joe turned, then pointed at the ground. "There!" I looked just in time to see the last of the candies disappearing into a whirlwind of dust.

MADAME LORRAINE'S COMMENTS:

All healing isn't physical. Sometimes the spirit needs to be healed as well.

A disease of the soul is perhaps the most hideous sickness known to humankind.

Unfortunately, it's usually innocent people who feel its full effects. To become cured of such a disease, those afflicted with it must face the consequences of their actions and atone for the damage they have caused others. Sometimes the bitter medicine takes the form of suffering; sometimes it takes the form of service.

In Dr. Itherman's case, the universe has prescribed a long period of service after death to make up for a long period of self-interest and gross incompetence during life.

Dr. Itherman's spirit, currently in a state of repentance, is learning to accept his position as The Janitor. The best we can do for him is to leave him alone to do his job, although it may take him quite some time to clean up his mess.

THE LEGEND OF THE LAUREL HIGHLANDS

THE LEGEND OF THE LAUREL HIGHLANDS

NAME: *Ajap*
LOCATION: *Secret*
MANIFESTATION: *If one happens upon Ajap or is given the secret location, Ajap may communicate his wisdom through words, symbols, signs or an unlikely coincidence.*

We endured a day of rain while in search of a ghost we had dubbed Nobody. While we didn't know his name or background, we did know that he had died in the area about thirty years ago. We didn't find him, which I guess is what usually happens when you set out to find Nobody. The only thing we got out of our investigation was soggy. The rain stopped around seven o'clock and Joe, our campfire expert, was trying to start a fire with wet wood when Red showed up bearing gifts—a cart full of dry timber, a tuna casserole, homemade bread and a cherry pie.

"Red, this is great," Chelley said, dishing out the food onto paper plates. We took our share and began to eat as we watched Red, a true campfire expert, build us a warm, cozy fire.

After dinner we reviewed our day's work. Red sat near us and listened in, taking an occasional sip from a silver flask he kept in the pouch of his hooded sweatshirt. He generously shared his spirits and I, not wanting to insult him, added a dash of whiskey to my coffee.

We decided that our investigation into Nobody was over, at least as it related to this collection. He was too elusive, too sketchy, and we had spent too much effort trying to pin him down. It was time to move on.

As we sat around the fire, I suggested that we consider investigating the Legend of the Laurel Highlands. Even if we decided not to investigate it, I could at least tell everyone the story.

"I know that tale," Red said, nodding with enthusiasm. "I'd sure like to hear it again." The others murmured in agreement. There was no doubting that Red had become another unexpected, albeit informal, addition to our team.

"Yeah, let's hear it," Tricia said, passing the flask to Joe.

Without further coaxing I told my story.

My Grandpa Mike told me the Legend of the Laurel Highlands one summer night during a camp-out when I was around eleven years old. It's the story of a tribe of noble warriors who lived in the Laurel Highlands long before the Europeans arrived.

I remember sitting near a small campfire with my cousins Joanne, Peggy, Gregory, Stan and Theresa. Even though we were camping out in my aunt's backyard, just one house away from my home, to us it was like being miles away in a dark wilderness. It had rained earlier that evening and a thick fog was settling in around us. Although we acted brave, inside I knew we were all a little scared of the silent darkness. When a barn owl suddenly began hooting, we all let out a shriek and ran into the musty army tent—but not as bad as yours, Chelley—that was to be our sleeping quarters for the night.

Gregory was the first to recover his wits. "Hey, it's just an old owl," Gregory said, with an exasperated flick of his wrist. He scrambled outside. "Come on out. It's safe, you sissies."

One by one we made our way back to the fire and began to talk about everyday things, chattering like a flock of crows.

Some time later, Peggy tapped me on the shoulder. "What's that?" she said, pointing to a dark, shrouded figure walking toward us. Once again, we all screamed and dived back into the tent.

"It's me. Grandpa," announced a familiar voice. "Grandma popped some corn for you." We made our way back to the fire and helped ourselves to the popcorn. I felt like an idiot, but at least we were all idiots.

After the popcorn was gone, Grandpa got up to leave. "Where're you going, Grandpa?" I asked. "Why don't you stay and tell us a story?" My grandfather's nickname was Preacher, and he got it because he was the best storyteller in the whole county. When I was younger, I used to readily believe his "true stories" about ghosts, demons and other things that went bump in the night, but now that I was more mature, I was very skeptical of the truthfulness behind his tales. But I loved and respected him so much I humored him, allowing him to believe that I still believed.

Grandpa appeared to hesitate.

"Please?" Stan begged him. Soon we were all begging him.

"Alright," he sighed, appearing to give in to us, when it was clear to me that he'd had no real intention of leaving without spinning a yarn first. He crouched down beside the fire, and the red glow of the flames added color to his pale cheeks. I could tell he was searching for the perfect story befitting the misty, mysterious nature of the night. Finally, a slight smile creased his face and he began.

"This is the Legend of the Laurel Highlands. It is as ancient as these mountains and as lasting as the streams that run through our valleys. I first heard it from an Indian trader named Paja Sam. Since then I've heard it told a thousand times by the locals. It was always told the same way, using the same words, and it must always be told that way.

"On an evening much like this one, Paja Sam drove his horse-drawn wagon into town. He was selling notions, puzzles, candies, cloth, knickknacks and the like. He also entertained his customers with a little show, dancing Indian dances and singing Indian songs. I was in awe of his long, black braids and the beaded threads woven into his hair, but there was something else wonderful about him that I never told anyone. A golden spirit in the shape of a huge eagle stood next to him the whole time he chanted his Indian songs, but I seemed to be the only one who could see it.

"Before I pass the legend on to you, we must call upon the spirit that I saw that evening." Grandpa Mike stood up and spread his hands over the fire. "Oh Great Spirit, who cleanses and purifies us, we call upon you to join us in passing on the Legend of the Laurel Highlands."

He turned toward us. His voice dropped to a whisper. "If I am indeed permitted to pass on the legend to you, a green flame will shoot out of the fire," he explained gravely. "That is a sign that the Great Spirit has arrived." We sat motionless, silently awaiting the spirit's answer. A few tense minutes passed, and it looked as though we were not ready to hear the legend after all. Suddenly a green flame sprang up in the middle of the fire and flickered steadily.

"It is so," Grandpa said, bowing slightly. "I have been honored this evening," he said, and faced us. Sitting down next to me, he whispered, "Pay close attention, young ones, for you have been chosen to be Keepers of the Tale."

"Okay, Grandpa," I whispered back. I knew the appearance of the green flame was nothing more than an old Girl Scout trick; a penny dropped into hot embers would heat up and release green gases. Still, I wanted to hear the story. Sometimes Grandpa was a silly old man, but I loved him dearly.

Grandpa cleared his throat, paused a moment, then launched into the story.

"Long, long ago, before the railroads cut through the mountains, before our streams were polluted with sulfur, before these many houses dotted the hillsides, there lived a nation of people called Malih 'lad, or the Nation of Many Colors. It was here, in this time and place, that people lived together in harmony, each in service to the other. There were no wars, no prisons, and no killing, for the people held sacred the creation of life. They believed that it was through individual expression that their god, Lani Girogira, came to know Itself.

"Among the Malih' lad was a wise mystic whose compassion and strength led her people. Her name was Enaida Fono Om. When Enaida turned 120 years old, she gave birth to her first child, a son whom she named, Ajap Retlaw, which means "oneness". Enaida had foreseen the Mot d'na Ydnic—The Last Day of All—and she hoped that her son would be the salvation of her people. Enaida trained Ajap in the ways of prophecy and sacred sight. Many times she told him about the manchild who, upon his sixtieth birthday, would turn from the tribe. He would tear apart the tribe's sacred totem, the Oklahem—the Complete Circle of Truth—and scatter its pieces into the mountains and beyond the great oceans.

"'I will never allow that to happen,' he vowed to his mother. 'I will die first.'

"On Ajap's sixtieth birthday, the tribe gathered in Enaida's dwelling to celebrate the passing of the Oklahem from Enaida to her son. This was right and fitting, since Ajap had proven himself to be kind and judicious. It was the highest of honors, for only one person could know the secrets of the Oklahem.

"Enaida closed her eyes as her held her son's hands tightly in hers and the transfer of the Oklahem's spirit began. Suddenly Enaida saw the face of the destroyer—and it was her beloved Ajap. Try as she might, she could not call back the truth from Ajap that she had already given him. He had grown much too strong for her. As he pulled the rest of the Oklahem from her, he pulled her life into him.

"The tribe gasped in terror as Enaida slumped to the ground.

"Ajap wept over his beloved mother's lifeless body. His tears fell not only for her but for himself, for he had seen his face in his mother eyes, the face of the destroyer. 'How can this be so?' he cried to the sky above. 'I am not he!'

"Soon after his mother was returned to the earth that had given her life, Ajap decided to leave the tribe, for he had no desire to bring destruction to his people and their way of life. 'I will serve you from a distance,' he promised them. He then instructed them to never allow him to enter their nation again. 'You must kill me if I walk but one inch onto this sacred ground,' he told them. 'I have but one request, that twelve of my brothers and sisters accompany me into the wilderness to protect you against me.'

"Immediately twelve of Ajap's tribal members stepped forward: Keaps, the poet, whose skill with both the written and spoken word gained him much respect from his clan. Sirk, head of the Malih 'lad council, whose gifts of energy and healing were often sought by those who were ill. Roth, the fiercely loyal companion to Enaida and father of Ajap. Laer Ra, a woman of great honesty who was Ajap's faithful companion. Sayala Mih, Enaida's youngest, who was blessed with great physical prowess. Niloc L' Lewop, who assigned everyone's daily chores. Setarcos, the oldest living member of the clan who often provided Enaida with wise counsel. Era Epsekash, a gifted artist who had discovered a new color. Nos Divad, a midwife known far and wide for her knowledge and compassion. Elam-Elameph, Ajap's teacher, renowned for his ability to reason, who had loved Enaida from a distance. And finally, two sisters: Aves, a fabled weaver of tapestry, whose creations seemed to flow from her fingers without planning, and Asereth, the only one entrusted with the duties of cooking and preparing sacred foods.

"Taking only a few supplies, the thirteen made their way across two mountain tops and came to rest near a river where two large identical rocks jutted out of the water. 'Here,' Ajap proclaimed, falling to his knees in prayer, 'is our new home—the Land of the Twin Rocks.'

"They lived there for two years, learning the ways of this strange forest. Sometimes, Ajap found himself longing for home. Often, in the still of the night, he would transport his spirit back to the Malih 'lad to make certain his people were safe.

He would visit his mother's grave to speak with her about his new life, and she would counsel him. They never mentioned the vision or The Last Day of All.

"One night Ajap was wakened by a great cry, as though a million voices were calling to him. He ran from his tent to the center of camp where the others joined him.

"'We have heard it too,' Setarcos said, bowing his head. 'Our people are gone. Our own end is near. The earth is unleashing herself upon us and we shall be destroyed.'

"At that moment Ajap understood the vision that he and his mother had shared. He was not the destroyer. He was the Apurk—the Chosen One—entrusted with saving the Oklahem from destruction. 'Our way will live on,' he promised his twelve companions. 'I am not to be feared. I am not the destroyer of the Oklahem but its preserver. Now we must hurry, for the earth calls us to itself.'"

"Ajap gathered them all into a circle and took his place in the center. 'Are you willing to be transformed to protect the One Great Truth?' he asked them.

"Without hesitation they all agreed. Ajap instructed Sirk to create two energy bonds: one between the earth, thirteen trees and themselves, and another bond between himself and the others. Sirk obeyed. Lines of pure light rose from the ground and crossed, forming a ball of energy that enveloped them all.

"'Great Lani Girogira, it is your will to call our nation home,' Ajap began as he crossed his arms over his chest. 'We ask that the Oklahem be torn apart and a fragment of it stored within each of your servants. If we each hold a Negam—a piece of your Cosmic Puzzle of Truth—we may protect the Oklahem and the power it holds. We will come together in the Glinerts, the Great Gathering , when Mot d' na Y'dnic threatens to descend upon those that follow us. We be the patient bearers of wisdom and will serve and guide the Han'na Ha' Vas-Xam, those who search for what is not lost. Send our spirits into the trees, allow us to be your Apurks, your Chosen Ones. This I ask only once, for I know my prayer is heard.'

"At once, the great Lani Girogira reached its mighty hand down from the heavens and touched the hearts of Ajap and his followers. Their prayer was answered. One by one the last of Ajap's clan fell to the ground. One by one their spirits soared high. One by one they received a Negam, and finally each was placed into a different tree. The twelve were dispersed to many lands, each one far away from the others.

"Keaps was entrusted with Grace and Communication, and he took his place in a palm tree. Sirk was given health and leadership and entered into a pine. Roth received purification and loyalty, and united with a speckled birch. Ajap's lovely Laer Ra was granted Honesty and disappeared into a cherry tree covered with pink blossoms. Sayala Mith obtained power and discernment, and Niloc L' Lewop received Order. They became the unbreakable Teak and Mahogany. Setarcos carried Wisdom to his home in the fragrant Hemlock, and the colorful Maple absorbed Era Epsekash, who filled the tree with Creativity and Vision. The willow's slender arms reached out for Nos Divad, who was graced with Resilience and Rebirth. The towering Fir embraced Elam and his gift of Balance. Aves

entered the Ash and with her carried Intuition. Finally Aserth, filled with intregrity, was embedded in the noble Cedar.

"Ajap was now alone, the last of his kind. 'I am ready,' he told the Great Spirit. 'Do with me as you will.'

"At that moment of complete surrender, Ajap came to understand the true meaning of the Oklahem. He had witnessed the Complete Circle of Truth in the coming together and separation of his mother, his nation and the Oklahem itself. He knew that someday those great nations that followed would live the Oklahem, not just carry it within themselves. But until that day, no one person would hold the all the truth.

"He lay on the ground and kissed the earth for the last time. 'Do you have a final prayer?' he heard his God ask him.

"'Yes," he answered. 'I wish to live in the mighty Oak in the Land of the Twin Rocks.'"

"His final prayer was granted. To this day Ajap Retlaw lives in the great oak in the Land of Twin Rocks. Surrounding him are twelve trees, memorials to his twelve companions, who protect him in times of danger."

My grandfather fell silent. He bowed his head low. The tale was over.

"Cool story, Grandpa," Joanne said. Everyone nodded in agreement.

"You must not repeat this story until you can tell it word for word," Grandpa warned us in a stern voice. "Nothing can be added, nothing can be deleted, for this is the story of the great nation of the Malih'lad. So be it."

That night, I couldn't get Grandpa's dramatic story out of my head. Dreams of Ajap, Enaida and the Oklahem danced through my mind. I woke believing that there might be some truth hidden in my grandfather's tale. What parts were true I wasn't sure.

When I questioned him about certain aspects of the story, he suggested that we seek out Ajap Retlaw and ask him. Surprised by his answer, I followed him to the end of town. We walked along the old railroad right-of-way for a few minutes, then climbed a hill. I found myself in a small clearing. In the middle was a huge oak tree, surrounded on the back and sides by smaller oaks. It looked as if the lesser trees were guarding the old one.

"This is Ajap," he whispered with such reverence that I genuflected and blessed myself with the sign of the cross.

"Well?"

"Well, what?" I asked. I felt awed, as if I were in the presence of The Almighty.

"Do you want to ask him a question?"

"Sure. Why not?"

My grandfather explained that I must perform a ritual called the Eiggam. "If you ever suspect that a tree is an Apurk," he instructed, "you can seek guidance from it, but you must do it in a certain way. First, you must salute the tree by crossing your arms over your chest and bowing slightly in the direction of the tree. Then walk up to it, place the palm of your right hand on its trunk and turn your left palm upward. Repeat the invocation I give you three times aloud."

I did has he instructed. As I stood, my hand on the tree's trunk, I said three times, "I seek unity, for in unity is peace."

My grandfather told me to ask the tree a question, either aloud or silently. I whispered mine. "Dear A...Ajap," I began, stuttering slightly. I had never talked to a tree before and the idea made me feel a little nervous. "My grandfather told me your story, and I was just wandering if it were true. Is it?" I added, remembering that my request had to be in question form.

I then backed away three steps and thanked the tree.

"Now, child," my grandfather explained, "the answer to your question may happen in an instant or may not reveal itself for years and years. The answer may come in the form of words, actions, symbols, signs or an unlikely coincidence. You must be patient if patience is demanded. When you discover the answer, you must be prepared to accept any change it may require, for the answer itself is useless without your willingness. Never repeat the question," he warned. "This shows a lack of trust. Do not seek the answer. It will find you."

"The end," I said.

Joe, Tricia, Chelley and Red applauded my story. We all said good-night to Red, just as the 704 Westbound met the 501 Eastbound. Red said something, which I couldn't hear because of the collision. I assumed Red was wishing us a pleasant evening, so I waved to him and retired to my tent.

As I lay on my cot, I couldn't help but replay the legend I had just narrated. Off and on over the years I had recalled the tale of Ajap and the Malih'lad, which eventually faded into a wonderful childhood memory of my Grandfather Mike and his delightful gift of storytelling. As I matured, I saw the "message" or "moral" of the story, but during those three weeks on the trail spent hunting for ghosts, I came to believe in more than messages and morals.

I drifted into the deep forest of my own dreams where my grandfather appeared to me as a talking rain cloud. I woke up not remembering anything he had said but feeling as if I were in for an adventure.

I stumbled out of the tent around seven o'clock. The sky was clear and blue. The grass was covered with dew and a gray squirrel dangled for a second from the limb of a nearby maple tree before righting himself. I don't know why, but the sight of Red lying flat on his back on the bare ground next to the smoldering embers of our campfire didn't surprise me.

"He's not dead, is he?" Tricia whispered, coming up behind me.

"God, I hope not." I hesitantly walked over to the motionless man and gently touched his elbow.

"Quit hogging the covers," he mumbled, rolling onto his stomach.

"I'll get a blanket for him," Tricia said, and disappeared into her tent. She came back with a small checkered quilt, which I tucked around Red. I then asked Joe to inform Mrs. Lanzenski that Red had spent the night at our campsite. Joe returned with a basket of fresh blueberry muffins and informed Mr. Lanzenski that he'd better get his butt home, which he did without delay.

We breakfasted on Mrs. Lanzenski's muffins, then headed up the trail in search of our next subject, the ghost of Roy E. O'Hara.

Just as we were about to call it a day, we passed the path that my grandfather and I had taken so long ago during our visit to Ajap, and I thought to myself, What the heck! I was investigating ghosts; why not see if that old oak was still standing?

I asked Chelley for the camera, then told everyone to return to the camp where I would meet up with them later. I made my way up the path to the familiar clearing in the middle of the woods. Much to my delight, the oak was still standing. In fact, it looked much the same as when I had first seen it. Its leaves were full and green, its limbs reached high and stretched far. Its "secret service" of smaller oaks still stood at attention around it. I got that same old feeling that I was in a church, standing in the presence of God. I saluted the tree but chose not to ask any questions. It knew what I was searching for. As I backed away I snapped a picture of Ajap the Apurk that lived in the oak in the Land of Twin Rocks.

The next day, Chelley took the film to be developed and put a rush on it, since we were leaving town at the end of the week. She picked up the photos an hour later and returned to camp, where she sought me out and took me aside. "What happened to this poor tree?" Chelley asked, handing me a photo. "Is it dead?"

I stared at the picture, caught somewhere between disbelief and amazement. The tree I took a picture of just a day ago was wearing its summer dress of bright green leaves. In this picture, the very same tree was as naked as a newborn baby.

"Hardly," I answered, clasping the picture over my heart. "It's just answering a young girl's question."

MRS.
RUSHINSTUPH

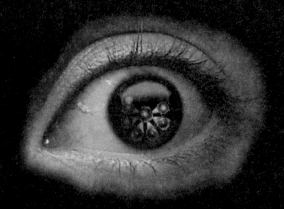

MRS. RUSHINSTUPH

NAME: *Mary Margaret Rushinstuph,* nee *Crupinka*

LOCATION: *Anywhere on the trail*

MANIFESTATION: *Felt nearly every day, but only by those wearing a necklace of any sort. Mrs. Rushinstuph is an equal-opportunity spirit: she manifests to men and children as well as to women. Those encountering this forlorn specter report feeling icy fingers at the back of their neck; some have reported smelling the scent of cinnamon.*

very family has its secrets—the uncle who drinks too much, the cousin whose mailing address is the state penitentiary, the aunt who got pregnant out of wedlock. Twice. It's all part of being a family. Actually, it's probably the most interesting part. According to Julia Crupinka, the big embarrassment in her family was her great-great aunt on her mother's side, Mary Margaret Rushinstupf. After hearing Julia's family story, I believe that Mary Margaret Rushinstuph may be the trail's resident black sheep.

We met Julia at my parents' house for a barbecue supper. Julia, a very distant relative, had moved to Cleveland, Ohio years ago. She had returned to her hometown of Twin Rocks to observe the Blacklick Township Sesquicentennial, 1850-2000 celebration, involving Twin Rocks, Vintondale, and Belsano.

It was early evening; my dad was fixing tuna steaks on the grill while my mother was busy preparing one of her specialty tossed green salads. I could tell Julia was a bit nervous as I watched her pace back and forth on the deck that overlooks my mother's colorful flower garden. A breeze blew over us, scented with the cloying, funereal fragrance of gardenias.

"You're going to think I'm crazy," she said, stopping to take a sip of ice tea from her glass.

"Julia, I have a Ph.D. in ghostology," I said, laying my hand on her shoulder. "As for them…." I pointed to Chelley, Tricia and Joe, who were tossing pretzels to my father's ancient Golden Retriever, Tugger. "They make a living tracking down disembodied spirits." The crew overheard me and gave us a toothy grin. "If anything, I'd say we are the ones who are a little touched in the brain."

"Yes," she said, smiling knowingly. "I see what you mean. Mind if I tell you a family tale? I think you'll be interested, given your profession. Maybe the others would like to hear it, too."

I asked the crew to join us. It was story time. Then I asked my parents if they wanted to listen to the story but both said they had heard it before. At Julia's request, we have not included her picture in this book. However, Chelley did an ink rendering of Miss Ruskinstupf and the Prince of Darkness, based on Julia's descriptions of them.

"My great-great aunt," Julia began, staring into the distance, "was hauntingly beautiful. Chestnut hair…dark, warm eyes…skin as white as cream and as smooth as silk. She was a small, delicate creature, almost like a fairy princess. I guess that, if you saw her today, you'd say she had 'good genes.' Men from all over the county sought her hand in marriage. They were entranced by her beauty. I once saw an old sepia-tone photograph of her, taken in her glory days. She was standing by the gate to her garden, surrounded by white gardenias and hollyhocks. She was wearing a flowing dress and an unusual necklace. Behind her was a statue of a handsome but evil-looking man, holding a small child. She was stretching out her hand, as if beckoning me to join her, and believe me, she was so enchanting that, if I could have, I would have climbed into that picture to be with her."

"Where is the picture?" I asked, hoping that she still had it in her possession.

"My great-grandfather had it buried with him. It was his dying wish that the necklace be buried with him, but since it was of such great value to my family, they did what they believed to be the next best thing: They buried that picture of Aunt Mary wearing it.

"I tried to get them to bury the necklace, because I understood the significance of his request. So did my Aunt Cecile, who inherited it from her Aunt Violet, who, sort of "inherited" it from Aunt Mary, as you'll soon find out. The necklace...." Julia's voice trailed off. She stood in silence, lost in her thoughts, and she remained so for a short while until my father tapped her on the back.

"Here's your dinner, Jul. Hot off the grill." He held out a paper plate heaped with tuna, salad, and grilled red and green peppers.

Julia took the plate without a word and sat in the chair next to me, picking at her food.

"Did she get to the part about the devil?" my father asked, sitting down across from me. "I love that part."

"Dad," I warned, chewing on a piece of tuna. "Don't ruin the story."

At last Julia continued. "Mary was not only lovely, she was also lucky. She was like a cat. No matter what dangerous, foolish or horrible thing she did, she always landed on her feet. Her beauty was like an endless bank account and she drew on it regularly.

"After weighing her best marriage proposals—and she had plenty to choose from—she settled on a man thirty years her senior who had given her all sorts of expensive clothing and other gifts. Mr. Nicholas Rushinstupf was very wealthy. He had made his fortune buying land that he sold at a huge profit to the railroads. Unfortunately for Mary, after the wedding she discovered that Nicholas was as selfish as she was beautiful. She quickly came to realize that the money he had spent on her during their courtship was no more than an investment in a piece of property that he wanted, property that would produce him an heir to his fortune.

"Nicholas did have a large house, though it was austerely furnished, overrun with mice, and heated only by a single fireplace. To make matters worse, Nicholas was too stingy to employ servants. He expected Mary to do all the cleaning, cooking and other housework.

"Once Mary became aware of how tightfisted Nicholas was, she refused to succumb to his advances, so he began to force himself on her. The moment he discovered she was with child, he left her alone. Driven half-insane with revenge, Mary made Nicholas a special dinner one night, a spicy curry dish laced with poison she had originally intended to use on the mice. She didn't see him for two days. On the morning of the third day she smelled a foul odor coming from the basement. She didn't have to see his corpse to know it was there. Somehow she lugged his body into the garden shed and set it on fire. Burned to death in an accident, read the coroner's report.

Serves him right, Mary thought, happy to see how well her plan had worked. Then her plan went terribly wrong. Mary had assumed that she would inherit her husband's fortune but, shortly after Nicholas's death, she learned that the old skinflint had left all his money to his older brothers, Ivan and Igor. They generously agreed to let her remain in the house, but only if she took care of it without pay.

"Mary figured that no one worth knowing would want a pregnant, penniless widow, and marriage to another old miser was not in her plans. So she feigned a miscarriage and hid her growing belly underneath loose, black clothing. She avoided seeing people as much as possible, preferring to stay cloistered in the house, 'in mourning' for her dear, dead husband.

"The townsfolk thought of Mary as a true lady and a first-class wife. It was too bad about the baby, they said, but there was no use questioning God's will.

"They didn't know that God's will had nothing to do with Mary's schemes for her future. When her labor pains started, she made her way deep into the forest that surrounded Nicholas' estate. Eventually she collapsed, exhausted, on a patch of bare ground surrounded by massive stones that had been pushed into the Pennsylvania Highlands by a melting glacier at the end of the Ice Age. The locals called it Satan's Ring and forbade their children to play there."

I nodded, as I knew the place very well. My parents had warned me to stay away from Satan's Ring, for it was bathed in the blood of little children who disobeyed their parents' warnings. Actually, it was a dangerous area. To get there involved climbing over huge boulders. A person could easily slip between them and become stuck, or fall into one of the many pits, said to be the home of deadly rattlesnakes. Since Satan's Ring is located about two miles into the forest, the likelihood of anyone hearing screams for help is next to none.

"Mary's labor soon grew intense," Julia continued. "As she pushed and strained to rid herself of her 'inconvenience,' she debated what to do with it and toyed with the idea of dropping it into the deepest pit among the rocks, leaving it for dead. After she finally gave birth, she cut the umbilical cord and wiped the baby clean with an old rag she had brought with her. She laid the naked infant on a rock and watched as it wiggled about. It was a little girl, as red and wrinkled as a shrunken old lady.

"'My, but you're ugly,' she said to it, slipping out of her bloodied dress. She stood naked on the rocks, rubbing her still-distended stomach. "I'm glad you're out of my belly. Why, I'd be doing you a favor to toss you away. Why anyone would want the likes of you, I'll never understand.'

"At that moment, the names of Mr. and Mrs. Germane Smith popped into her head. They were a wealthy but childless couple whom the congregation of the church prayed for every Sunday. And then there were the Deninglers, who also longed for a child. That's when Mary realized that she could profit from her predicament if she made a good deal. Lots of couples probably would do anything to get their hands on a healthy baby. The child would go to the highest bidder.

"'I'd would like to make an offer, Mary,' came a satiny voice from the pit.

"Mary reached for her clothes and held them up to her. 'Who's there?' she called, looking about.

"'Let's just say I'm an old friend of Mr. Godot,' she heard the voice purr from a nearby tree. 'We haven't spoken for a while, ever since our little…disagreement over real estate. He had a pet name for me—Lucifer. But you can call me Luke.'

"'Lucifer is the Devil's name,' Mary said, as she quickly dressed. "You stay away from me. I want nothing to do with you. Go away.'

"'Too late. I'm here. You called for the highest bidder, and I'm here to make my bid. You determine if it's high enough.' And there he was, all of a sudden, standing right in front of her, dressed in an elegant black satin suit with a crimson ascot and cummerbund, his head crowned with a top hat. The phrase 'You handsome devil' was probably created with just such an image in mind. Much to Mary's surprise, Satan did not have horns. Well, none that were readily apparent, even when he tipped his hat to her. He didn't stink of sulfur either. Instead, the scent of cinnamon wafted from him like perfume.

"'Surprised at my beauty?' he asked as he picked up the whimpering baby and cradled her in his arms. 'Everyone is. I don't know who started the rumor of that whole hooves-and-pitchfork thing. I suspect it was Aphrodite. That woman had one hell of a jealous streak. I don't have a tail, either. Want to see for yourself?' The strange gentleman began to unbutton his gleaming trousers.

"'No, sir, please,' Mary said, staring at him in amazement. 'I shall take your word for it. What is your business with me?'

"Suddenly he disappeared with the baby, only to reappear a few seconds later atop one of the great rocks. 'Now, Mary,' he said with an indulgent smile. 'Didn't I just say I was here to make an offer on your...goods? I can give you something that no one else can, lovely lady, if you but allow me to adopt this miserable waif, whom you have no need for, I might add.'

"'What do you mean by "something"?' Mary asked, then listened quietly as Luke made her a simple, straightforward offer: If he got the baby, Mary would get everlasting beauty.

"Once again he appeared in front of her. 'Read and sign on the dotted line,' he said, pulling a printed document out of the air and handing it to Mary. 'It's an "adoption" agreement. Remember,' he warned, 'read the fine print before you sign.'

"He pulled a fountain pen out of the top of his head and handed it to the astonished girl. But as Mary prepared to sign the paper, Luke stopped her. 'Are you sure you understand the part about the necklace?'

"Mary nodded. She had read everything, including the fine print, and she was satisfied with the terms. As Luke watched her write her name upon the paper, saliva began to drip from his mouth. 'Wonderful, wonderful,' he said, drawing two glasses of blood-red wine from the same invisible cabinet he had reached into to obtain the paper. "Let's celebrate our good fortune. Cheers!" Mary sipped from the glass, pleased that, in her mind, she had made the better of the bargain.

"'Now I must be on my way, my dear." Luke threw the glass into the air, where it vanished at once. 'But before I go—the necklace.' He reached into his breast pocket, then searched

his coat pocket, then finally found what he was looking for in his beautiful top hat. He withdrew a gold chain, on which hung a large gold pendant studded with amethysts, each the size of a small grape. Diamonds glittered between the deep purple gemstones. It was lovely in a painful sort of way, and Mary could not shake the notion that the necklace had been torn from the neck of a dying woman.

"'Pretty little bauble, isn't it?' Luke said, fastening the chain around her throat. 'Remember, you must never take it off. Do you recall reading what will happen if human hands—yours or those of another—remove it from your neck?'

"'Yes,' Mary whispered. She remembered very clearly. 'My beauty will fade in an instant. Otherwise, it will go on forever.' Beyond that, she knew nothing.

"'Excellent,' Luke said, and before Mary could thank him, he and her child were gone. Two black butterflies fluttered about her head for a moment, then disappeared into the shadows of the woods.

"Luke had promised her eternal beauty, and he made good on his promise. Mary stayed ravishingly beautiful, year after year, as delightfully lovely as on the day she had met the Devil at Satan's Ring. But when all those around Mary grew old and died while she remained untouched by Father Time's caresses, ugly rumors began to flit around her. People claimed to have heard a baby crying in the woods every now and then, but no abandoned baby was ever found. Others wondered why Mary was never seen without her necklace, which, as beautiful as it was, certainly did not complement all her clothing. The older townsfolk began warning unruly children to behave, lest they grow up victims of 'unholy bargains, like Mary Margaret Rushinstupf.'

"My Great-aunt Violet, just a girl of twelve at the time, was consumed with finding out what sort of secret power, if any, lay behind her aunt's necklace. Determined to discover the truth, one night she crept to Mary's bed as she tossed and turned in fitful dreams. Since she had heard rumors claiming that Mary had received the necklace from an evil source, Violet decided to test this idea. 'I'm back, and I've come for my necklace,' Violet said, as she stood over her aunt. She had no idea what sort of reaction such a statement might have on Mary, but she was confident it would elicit some sort of reaction.

"Suddenly Mary, still asleep, sat up in bed and clasped the pendant to her chest. 'No, you don't, Satan,' she muttered, her eyes still shut in troubled slumber. 'You got the brat, I got the beauty. I've lived up to my part of the bargain, now you live up to yours.'

"Shocked and frightened by this hideous revelation, Violet decided immediately to try to free her aunt from the contract that had doomed her to unnatural youth. Seizing the chain, Violet tugged hard and ripped the necklace from Mary's throat. Imagine her surprise, disgust and disappointment when her brave act, far from freeing Mary, reduced her instantly to a heap of bones inside a wrinkled, sagging bag of skin, barely recognizable as a human being, much less a former enchantress.

"Without her necklace, Mary was cursed to walk this earth as a withered, loathsome-looking spirit, crippled so badly with arthritis that she had shrunken to nearly half her original height. They say she haunts the trail looking for the necklace. Her icy fingers can be felt on the nape of your neck as she tries to undo whatever chain, cord or choker you might be wearing.

"Violet believed that, if Mary ever got hold of the enchanted necklace, no one would ever be able to free her soul or the soul of her infant daughter. So Violet became the first Keeper of the Purple Necklace. Once the Keeper died, she decreed in her will, the necklace must be passed on for safekeeping to the eldest daughter in the family, ad infinitum, from generation to generation. The new Keeper was sternly cautioned never to wear the necklace or let anyone else wear it.

"My aunt Cecile died recently," Julia said, looking up at me. "She left me, the eldest daughter, to carry on the tradition." With that Julia removed a small velvet box from her purse and lifted its lid. Inside the box lay the purple necklace, just as she had described it.

"What happens if you put it on?" I asked, afraid to even touch the thing.

"I don't know," Julia answered. "And I don't want to find out."

MADAME LORRAINE'S SUGGESTION: *Although this spirit is not known to be dangerous, she is tainted with evil and should be avoided. Try to prevent contact with her altogether by not wearing anything around your neck. This includes all necklaces and anything resembling a necklace,*

such as chains, chokers, leather thongs, cords, beads, pearls, garlands, lanyards and so on. Even shirt collars have been known to attract Mary's attention, however, so there's no way to guarantee you won't encounter her.

Unfortunately, there is nothing you can do to help this wretched soul who is doing penance for her heartless deeds. When she gains enough insight to cease looking for her charmed necklace, thus putting vanity behind her, she may find release. Until then, if you do contact her, put your fists together and rapidly pull them apart, as if you are breaking a string. This should frighten her away.

AUTHOR'S NOTE: *The cries of Mary's baby are still heard at Satan's Ring. I am preparing a special task force to investigate this phenomenon, which may involve confronting a powerful negative force.*

BIG BEAR CAVE

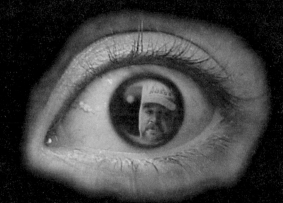

BIG BEAR CAVE

NAME: *Ben Ruskin*

LOCATION: *Anywhere along the Ghost Town Trail. The cave in this story has been called Big Bear Cave for at least a hundred years and has been the home of many bears. We are not disclosing the location of the cave because bears still inhabit it. Those of you who want to explore it do so at your own risk.*

MANIFESTATION: *Auditory only, never visual. Ben's cries have been likened to the screams of a torture victim or the shrieks of an animal trapped in a fire.*

WARNING: *Do not feed, chase or harm any deer or other animals you may encounter on the trail. It's dangerous to them, and it certainly could be dangerous for you.*

Joe left the campsite around six o'clock. His mission: Get us pizza from Twin Rocks Pizza. I had guaranteed the crew that it was the best-tasting pizza in the tri-state area, and they were looking forward to proving me right. While we waited for Joe to arrive with our dinner, Red, who stopped by to visit, was teaching Chelley to build the ultimate campfire. Tricia was gathering summer flowers which she pressed on her portable Pres-a-Fleur gadget, and I was getting lessons from Madame Lorraine on how to develop my psychic ability. What little I had.

Around eight, Joe showed up with six large pizzas, two six packs of beer and a rather large, red-headed woman wearing cut-off jeans, work boots and a gray T-shirt emblazoned with large red letters reading TRUCK-U. I thought to myself that Joe had at last found the woman of his dreams, one I was sure his mother would love to call daughter-in-law.

"Why so much pizza, Joe?" I asked, taking the boxes from his arms.

"'S'good."

Joe's reasoning made sense to him, despite the fact that we now had seventy-two pieces of pizza and only seven people.

I introduced myself to Joe's newfound friend, a truckdriver he'd said he met at the pizza shop. "I'm J.B.," she said, ruffling the hair on top of my head with her massive hand. "I feel like I already know you," she said, with a hearty laugh. "Joe told me about your ghostbusting adventures. Did you two really get lost in the desert chasin' a ghost?"

I nodded.

"Lucky you didn't die," she said, ripping a beer from its plastic holder. "Once I was drivin' a rig through a snowstorm near Kalamath Falls, jackknifed and nearly frozen to death. Mother Nature is cruel, y'know. People who mess with that old lady find out that she can be one mean mother." J.B. laughed and slapped her thigh, impressed with her own witticism.

"J.B was telling me one whopper of a story while I was waiting for the pizza," Joe said. Lucky for us, she's agreed to tell it to us. But first, we'd better eat."

Joe wasn't joking. It was a good thing we ate first and listened to J.B.'s tale later, because it wasn't the prettiest story we'd ever heard. She did say that it was true, however, and I believed her. The ghost involved is well-documented. The following is a sanitized version of what J.B. told us that night.

Everyone in Twin Rocks and Vintondale agreed, Ben Ruskin was not the most likable of men. A hermit by choice and probably by nature, Ben lived by himself in a cottage in the woods. He grew his own vegetables and hunted wild game—both in and out of season.

Hunting not only put food on the table, it also gave Ben the deep, satisfying pleasure of the kill. Once he had shot a hummingbird, which disappeared in a puff of feathers. Another time he shot a bobcat deep in the woods. The thrill of the kill was sweetened by the fact that hunting such rare animals was strictly illegal.

Ben loved any challenging prey but deer were his favorite. Their big eyes made excellent targets, and so did their long, thin legs. The best sport was to shoot a deer one leg at a time until the animal collapsed in agony in a pool of blood. Then he'd finish it off with a shot between the hind legs. They never died right away, and it was interesting to watch how they squirmed and twisted about in the final throes of death. Fawns, with even thinner legs, provided the best sport of all. The only trouble was, two or three shots usually obliterated them.

On his rare excursions into town, Ben avoided conversation with anyone, speaking as few words as possible to get his needs across to the local grocer or hardware store owner. Those two used to say that they got the distinct impression that, if given half a chance, Ben would happily take just as many potshots at people as he did at animals.

For instance, they'd say, there was that thing with the dog, and then they'd tell about the time Ben went to Vintondale one hot summer day. He had come upon a Springer Spaniel puppy lying on the porch of a house near the town. The pretty little dog was partially obscured by a rocking chair and presented such an engaging target that Ben took aim at its fluffy head. Just then a tall, muscular man had come out of the house, shouting curses at him. Ben aimed his rifle at the man's chest, then lowered his weapon and began to walk away. "I was just fooling around," he mumbled.

The puppy's owner contacted the police, but the officer who showed up laughed the moment Ben's name was mentioned. "Keep your dog inside when you're not around," he told the tall man.

"But…well, the way he looked at me, you'd have thought I was depriving him of his last meal," the man insisted. "I thought for sure he was going to shoot me."

Nothing came of the incident, and of course, no one could prove that Ben actually did ever shoot anyone. Now and then people would get lost in his neck of the woods, but they almost always showed up again, hungry and cold, but alive. There were those occasional hunters who mysteriously disappeared, like Paul J. Henley and Kip Bower. Police believe they probably had a heart attack or stroke, fell dead in the woods and were eaten by wild animals. No remains were ever discovered. For a while it was whispered around town that Ben shot those two old men for nothing more than the sport of killing someone. Eventually the rumors faded, though, and, since the two hunters were not from the area, the townsfolk soon forgot about them. In Ben's defense, it must be said that people can be cruel, especially to those who are different from the rest. And there's no denying that Ben Ruskin was not your mainstream sort of fellah or the most popular guy in town.

Ben often complained that he was the victim of hard luck, which made him irritable. One day he had a streak of particularly hard luck that left him feeling particularly irritable. His social security check did not show up and he needed the cash to repair the leak in the roof of his cabin before the next storm rolled in. Unfortunately, an enormous black thundercloud was already rolling toward his place, and quickly too. Ben could smell the rain in the air. So doing what he always did to relieve tension, Ben grabbed his rifle and headed to the woods to shoot something. As usual, he really did not care what is was, as long as it could suffer and bleed.

Ben hadn't walked two miles along a narrow game path when he came upon every hunter's dream: five deer resting in a soft bed of pine needles under a grove of tall hemlocks. Easy targets, he thought to himself, and he wondered how many deer he could take down before they scattered into the woods. He took aim at a white-speckled fawn lying contentedly beside its mother. The way Ben figured it, if he got a few yards closer to the pair he could get both deer with one bullet. Now that was a challenge he couldn't resist. If he lay on the ground, he could shoot the fawn through the liver at just the right angle so that the bullet would enter the belly of the doe. The bullet might not kill the mother outright but it would sure tear up her innards good. She'd probably limp off into the woods and die eventually; her trail of blood would be easy to follow.

As Ben crept closer to make the kill, he became aware of an odd noise that sounded like a coal-powered locomotive releasing steam. The hair rose on the back of his neck and a sick feeling gripped his stomach. Suddenly something rammed him from behind and knocked him to the ground with such force that he had to struggle for breath. When he was finally able to look over his shoulder, he wished he hadn't. A monstrous buck with twenty points loomed over him, snorting and pawing the ground like a bull raging at a matador. The buck was bigger than any deer Ben had ever seen before, and though he was terrified he was also indignant. How dare this dumb animal spoil his shot!

On the other hand, he thought, this might be his lucky day. The buck's rack would look great on the wall above his fireplace.

"You stupid critter! I'll blow your legs off," he shouted, groping for his gun but finding nothing. When he looked around, he saw that his high-powered rifle with its telescopic sight had landed in some heavy underbrush. Only the very tip of the steel-blue barrel was noticeable.

The buck seemed to notice this too. Instead of running off, he let out a deep bellow, which was answered by his herd. From the shadows of the hemlocks, deer after deer glided into the clearing. There were too many for Ben to count. An icy ripple of fear passed slowly over his body as the deer trotted forward, surrounding the petrified man. Even he could make out the burning sparks of hatred smoldering in their large brown eyes.

Without warning, the immense buck reared up and lurched at Ben, angling his massive rack of antlers at Ben's belly. Scared out of his trance, Ben rolled to one side, sprang to his feet and began to run blindly into the shadows of the forest. *To hell with the gun!* he thought.

The herd followed closely behind him, the thunder of their hoofbeats mingling with the thunder that began to shake the heavens. A cold rain began to fall, and Ben began to shiver. They're forcing me toward Big Bear Cave, he thought. But that was a good thing. He fondled his razor-sharp gutting knife, safe in the scabbard hung on his belt. Even if those crazy deer tried to enter the narrow mouth of the cave, he could slit their throats one by one as soon as their heads appeared. Ben scrambled up the slight grade, squeezed into the cave's opening and hid in the safety of the darkness. He knew the cave had a reputation as a bear den, but he wasn't afraid. He had never seen a bear in the cave, and if there was one, why, he would cut its throat too.

"Damn dumb deer!" Ben screamed at the top of his lungs. "Think you can best a real man, do ya? I'll cut each and every one of you into chunks for venison stew. This isn't over yet."

And Ben was right. It wasn't over yet. The mighty buck loped up near the entrance of the cave, stopped just outside and gave a high-pitched cry, much like a bugle sounding a charge. Then Ben heard nothing for a while. The deer simply stood outside the cave, staring in at him. *They look like they're watching a goddamn TV show*, Ben thought, puzzled but relieved that the deer were too afraid to even try attacking him.

A gentle sound, like the sigh of a sleepy child, rose from the back of the cave.

Ben froze. Had he imagined the sound? He was frightened, cold and out of breath. Maybe he was hearing things.

There was another sigh, then a snuffling sound, then a muffled whine.

Ben turned and squinted into the darkness. He removed his knife from its scabbard and held it down at his side, pointing into the shadows. Whatever damn critter was in the cave with him, bear or human or anything else, he was taking it down. This was his cave now.

Ben heard the sound of slow, large shuffling steps. Two bright eyes shone through the blackness. A long snout and finally a head emerged—the shaggy black head of a gigantic bear. Its angry roar echoed throughout the cave. Ben didn't have to be a psychic to know what the bear was saying.

The hunter knew he had a choice to make, and whatever option he selected meant certain death, not for the animals, but for him. He could choose to be ripped apart by a grumpy bear—nothing personal—or stamped and prodded to pieces by a horde of avenging deer.

Ben thought he had a way out. Whipping his knife up against his throat, he prepared to slash it open. But out of the darkness flew a huge paw. Sharp claws raked his hand, tearing fingers from the knuckles. The knife fell to the ground with a puny clink.

Ben drew back in pain and fear. Now he had no choice but to go with the bear.

It was a quicker death than the one the deer had planned for him, although a painful death is probably never quick enough. Imagine having your belly ripped open by long, sharp fangs and your intestines sucked out of you like limp spaghetti. Then imagine being conscious enough to witness the whole thing and feel every moment of a pain so excruciating and relentless that you wish you could wrench your head off. You just might come close to imagining the pain that Ben felt during his last hour of life.

Although Ben's ghost has never been seen on the trail, his cries of agony often reverberate through the valley, sending a chill through those who walk the trail—both the living and dead. Animals, however, seem totally deaf to his screams.

Sadly enough for Joe, J.B. drove away in her truck later that evening. She was bound for the central warehouse of Tomater Plan-It, Inc.—the condiment manufacturer that "Puts the slop back in sloppy joes"—with a shipment of Insta-Cheez Bloc.

MADAME LORRAINE'S

COMMENT: *There is really nothing that can be done to help Ben move on before the universe itself decides it is time to release him.*
Sometimes we create our own purgatory where we must burn off our sins. Some of us may wish to thank our

lucky stars that deer are unable to load guns and point them at us.

SHOES

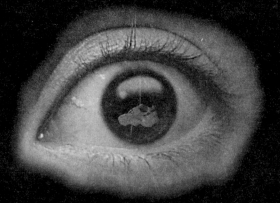

SHOES

NAME: *Roy E. O'Hara*

LOCATION: *Anywhere on the trail from Nanty-Glo to Dilltown. Shoes mainly hangs out at the first bench on the right after the trail intersects the paved gameland access road; this is about half-way between Twin Rocks and Vintondale.*

WARNING: *Make certain that your shoelaces are tightly tied. If you must remove your shoes, take them off one at a time. Never let them out of your grip.*

This is a wacky story that even I didn't believe when I first heard it. If it weren't for so many bikers and joggers leaving the trail shoeless, I wouldn't have given this tale a second thought. And, if Tricia hadn't fallen victim to the trail's resident thief, I would have passed on the whole story.

The tale involves Roy E. O'Hara. Yes, this is the same Roy E. O'Hara who created Insta-Cheez Bloc, the processed cheese food with imitation smoked cheddar flavoring that revolutionized the fast food industry. It all began on Roy's father's dairy farm on the outskirts of Twin Rocks. As with many great inventions, Insta-Cheez Bloc happened quite by accident. Roy, a young man of sixteen, was in the process of making cottage cheese, a job normally reserved for his older brother, Russell, when he bumped against a shelf and knocked over a can of turpentine he had been using to weigh down a tarp. A "wee bit" of the aromatic liquid spilled into the vat of curdling cheese.

Now, his family being somewhat less than well-to-do, Roy knew they could scarcely afford to waste the contaminated food. But Roy, being the innovator that he was, decided to cook the not-quite-ready-to-become-cottage-cheese over an open fire pit, hoping that the added heat would burn off the turpentine. Unfortunately, Roy was lured away from his task by bad timing: his father had chosen that moment to attempt a romantic union between his young Jersey bull and a neighbor's Ayrshire cow. The female being almost twice the size of the bull created an interesting set of logistics, and Roy simply could not pull himself away from the ensuing scene of marital confusion. He forgot about his cottage cheese experiment altogether, even after the bull and cow had been reconciled and led to separate stalls.

A few days passed. When Roy's brother told him to clean up the mess he had made behind the barn, Roy remembered the fire pit. He ran to see if he could rescue his concoction, but all that was left was a large amount of dull yellow powder. Fearing that he would be in serious trouble if he told his parents what had happened, Roy ladled the contents of the vat into an empty feed bag and lugged it into the storage room. A few days later, Roy's father discovered the bag. On the mistaken belief that the bag contained bran, he poured some of the powder into a bucket, added water and stirred. He thought he was making a bran mash for an ailing calf; instead, he was making food processing history. Right before his eyes, the powder coagulated into a lump, then formed a ball, and at last a large, solid block of cheese-like material.

Roy's father immediately showed the "weird bran" to Roy, who knew its real identity but chose not to reveal it. He broke off a small chunk of his creation and slowly slid it into his mouth. It felt and tasted like a mild, high-quality cheese, similar to ricotta, although it was as solid as a good cheddar, had aged only three days and cost pennies to produce.

"Is it any good?" his father asked.

For some perverse reason, Roy answered in the negative. "Tastes like crap," he said, placing the block back in the bag.

Soon his father had forgotten all about the "weird bran," but Roy was already beginning to develop a marketing plan.

Roy's life was far from happy, and he was always dreaming up ways to escape. His father treated him more like a servant than a son, and his mother was a hypochondriac who cared for no one's comfort but her own. Russell lay in wait for him and beat him to a pulp on a regular basis, just for "fun."

Worse yet, Roy was always the butt of jokes among his peers at school and church. A poor farm kid, he wore second-hand clothes that where either too big or too small and always out of style. His shoes where what the kids called "shit-kickers", large work boots inherited from his brother or father. They were invariably old and worn, and smelled like a barnyard. Roy hated the shoes more than any other emblem of his poverty, but there was nothing he could do about them. He saved up for a new pair of shoes once, but they quickly became just as disreputable as his old ones. What choice did he have? He had to have shoes.

When Roy finally left the farm, he left with no regrets. He took very little with him, only a Woolworth's suitcase containing his best clothes, a beat-up alarm clock, and a head full of hopes for his powdered cheese formula. He went to Pittsburgh where he found work at a hospital cafeteria, unloading boxes of supplies from trucks. This new life wasn't much of an improvement from life on the farm, and it would have been unbearable for the young inventor without the friendship of LeRoy Bennett.

LeRoy, a salesman who sold food products in bulk to government institutions, was always cracking jokes and telling stories. Roy thought the roly-poly LeRoy was the most entertaining person in the world, and, though he was naturally suspicious of people, Roy eventually learned to put his trust in LeRoy. He also continued working on his cheese product, refining and improving it. He even invented a synthetic cheddar flavoring to put a little more oomph in the taste department. One night, as the inventor prepared sloppy joes for LeRoy in Roy's shabby little apartment, he blurted out his discovery.

"I've created a new food," he said, "and I think we could make some money off of it." With the air of a magician performing a card trick, Roy produced a square of his dairy food-turpentine masterpiece from a cupboard.

"Here it is," he said, with a flourish of his hand. "Ain't it something?"

"It's something, all right," LeRoy said, eyeing the glossy white mass. "Question is, what?"

"I call it 'O'Hara's Miracle Cheese Sensation,'" Roy said, "but I'm open to suggestions." He described the product's unusual formation properties and its cost-effectiveness.

"Did you say cheese?" LeRoy gasped. "How long has it been in that cupboard?"

"Oh, about three days," Roy answered cheerily. "That's one of its many beauties. Unlike real cheese, it needs no refrigeration. And it tastes great. Here, try it!" Roy slashed off a few slices of Cheese Sensation and laid them on top of LeRoy's sloppy joe before the salesman could even raise his hand in protest. After considerable coaxing, LeRoy raised the sandwich to his mouth, closed his eyes, and took a bite. Then he smiled. "This is good...no, great. Sensational! A little yellow food coloring, and we really could have something here, Roy-boy. The only thing is, let's change the name, okay? Something a little jazzier, a little more modern." Thus was Insta-Cheez Bloc born, the product of a lucky accident and a lot of fast talking.

LeRoy was a shrewd marketer, and he had set aside a little capital in case some wonderful opportunity fell into his lap. And here it was—square, cheesy, and with a long shelf life.

Together the inventor and the salesman formed RoyLeRoy Foods International and set up a modest factory. A few months later, a famous fast food company signed a contract for a year's supply of Insta-Cheez Bloc. Two years later, nearly every fast food restaurant in the country was clamoring for the cost-efficient cheese food—and RoyLeRoy became a multi-billion dollar company, virtually overnight. New products followed in profusion, including Plant-Stake, a vegetarian Delmonico steak substitute, and Dairy Air, an ice-cream-like product in aerosol form. The company's web site, InstaCheezBloc.com, received a record number of hits the day the company went public.

Roy was at last a happy man. He traveled all over the world, three times. He spent a year traveling in France, the Netherlands and Switzerland, where he studied under the finest cheesemasters. Returning home, Roy, who was a decent, honest man, realized he was obligated to share some of his miraculous wealth. So he funded libraries, established scholarships, and gave generously to charities. His fabulous art collection, including artist Arnold Woldhar's only known lithograph of a cheese wedge, was one of the best in the world. He was the honored guest of kings, queens and astute politicians.

Unfortunately, Roy's life was shaken a few years later when his friend LeRoy died. The unfortunate marketer, his head probably still whirling from a new product meeting, stepped directly into the path of the Insta-Cheez Bloc Wagon, a giant advertising vehicle shaped like the popular cheese food product. He had literally been destroyed by his own creation.

Roy was devastated. If it hadn't been for the blossoming of true love, who knows what would have happened to him? Roy met Jessica King, heiress to the KrunchaDelic cereal fortune, at a White House fund-raising dinner. The attraction was powerful and mutual. Roy and Jessica dated for six months before becoming man and wife at the most spectacular wedding event of the year on the East Coast. In the resultant media blitz, Twin Rocks citizens were proud to claim Roy as a native son.

Roy and his bride had two beautiful daughters and two handsome sons, none of whom were ever allowed within ten miles of a dairy farm. "You'll get tetanus," Roy admonished them, but the real reason was more disturbing. Recollections of Roy's painful past haunted him daily. Most embarrassing of all was the memory of those miserable shoes with the gaping holes, ripped laces and obnoxious odor. Roy went to great lengths to purchase the most beautiful shoes he could buy: custom-made leather Italian wing-tips, loafers and dress shoes, even handmade sheepskin slippers and one-of-a-kind athletic shoes. Any shoe that suffered the smallest scratch or stain or sign of wear was discarded along with its mate. Still, he had nightmares in which his long-gone scruffy workboots attacked him, stomping his face and kicking his ribs.

But Roy's problem with his past went beyond footwear and prevented him from being truly happy. Ashamed of his poverty, he always lied about his upbringing, at the same time plying his parents and brother with money to keep their mouths shut. Roy told everyone he met that he was related to Irish nobility, and was, in reality, a direct descendent of Brian Boru, an ancient Celtic king. He had false documents prepared to prove this, and even went so far as to take his whole family to visit his "ancestral home" and "treasured relatives" in Ireland. Unknown to all but him, the "home" was a rented castle. The charming "relatives" he introduced to his family and friends were talented actors and actresses Roy had personally auditioned in Dublin beforehand. In his heart, Roy hated lying to Jessica and his children, but he felt he had no choice. He feared they would stop loving him once they knew his true background.

He never saw everyone in his real family again. When his parents died, he did not attend the funeral but shipped a beautiful hand-carved Carrera marble tombstone from Italy to be placed on their grave. His brother Russell continued to live on the family farm and tend a few milk cows. He never spent any of the money Roy had sent over the years, and rumor had it that he had buried the stash somewhere on his property. It seemed that Russell was a changed man. All he wanted was for his brother to return home, if only for a day, so that he could apologize to him in person for all the pain he had caused Roy in their early years together.

One spring morning almost fifty years after Roy left the farm, Russell's prayers were answered: Roy called him, begging to return home. Moved by the touching romantic movie, "My Life as a Dairy Farmer," Roy had concluded that poverty was nothing to be ashamed of and spilled his heart out to Jessica and his kids. Jessica had secretly been in contact with Russell and had known the truth for years. She and the children were only too happy to forgive the repentant imposter.

Then came the real moment of truth, when Roy returned to his legitimate family home. Roy's reunion with Russell was tender and loving. Many tears of happiness where shed that day, and Roy eagerly accepted Russell's apology for the way he had tormented his younger brother. Roy even agreed to stay on the farm for a few weeks, although his family opted for a hotel in Twin Rocks.

Over the next few days, Roy came to fully accept who he was and where he had come from. He was at peace with himself at last for the very first time.

But here the fate of the cheese food tycoon took a sour turn. One soft summer evening, as the crickets were calling and the fragrance of new-mown hay hung like perfume in the air, Roy was overcome with nostalgia. He set out into the sunset, dressed in his best "country attire" and custom-fitted Austrian hiking shoes. His aim was to take a twilight stroll through Twin Rocks, revisiting the places of his troubled youth in order to put them behind him.

Oddly enough, at the very moment of his awakening, Roy was put to sleep—permanently. A stranger passing through town encountered Roy on the road and was impressed by the mogul's expensive clothing. Having had one too many, the stranger saw Roy not as a distinguished man-of-the-world but only as a source of easy cash. He shadowed the multimillionaire and struck him down with a crowbar in a vacant lot on the edge of town. Did the stranger intend to kill Roy? No one knows. Although two people witnessed the crime, the murderer was never apprehended. What is known is that the assailant stole Roy's wallet and elegant trail shoes, and that Roy succumbed to his injuries a few days after the assault. The *Twin Rocks Reporter*, a now-defunct newspaper, committed its entire front page to the story, part of which appears below.

All of the Laurel Highlands is in mourning today for Twin Rocks native Roy Edgar O'Hara, inventor of the well-known Insta-Cheez Bloc and other food products. Mr. O'Hara, the victim of a vicious attack by an unknown assailant last Wednesday, passed away Saturday night in an undisclosed private hospital in Johnstown. The son of the late Henry and Bernice O'Hara of Twin Rocks, Mr. O'Hara was famous for his generous contributions to worthy causes, including Shoes for the Needy and the Society for the Protection of the Rights of Large Farm Animals. His trademark—a fixation with shoes—was the subject of a recent novel by super-writer Joan Dresham and a motion picture starring mega-star Gil Melbourne. Mr. O'Hara's collection of rare and antique shoes is considered the finest in the world.

The article concluded with this plea:

The family requests that, in lieu of flowers, donations should be sent to the Roy E. O'Hara Ecole du Fromage in Paris, the world's only college dedicated to the study of cheese.

Tributes on television and radio and in major magazines and newspapers followed. Expensive shoes became the latest fashion rage. For several months after the murder, the name Roy E. O'Hara was on everyone's lips. Then Gil Melbourne was involved in a minor drug deal, and Roy slowly faded from the national consciousness.

That's when the first reports of strange sightings on the Ghost Town Trail began to take everyone by surprise. People not normally given to public drunkenness swore that they had seen a mass of shoes floating along the trail. Joggers who had removed their shoes to check a blister or search for a pebble in their sock claimed that their sneakers had risen up into the air like a pair of magician's doves and disappeared. "I turned my back on my designer running shoes for two seconds," one runner complained to us, "and when I reached for them they were gone."

Eventually the phantom acquired a name—Shoes. A psychic brought in from Cleveland to investigate the matter was the first to connect the thefts with Roy E. O'Hara. She concluded that he was stalking the trail in a desperate effort to recover his lost shoes and restore his damaged dignity, or perhaps to seek revenge against the thief who had murdered him. Along the way he had acquired quite a collection of footgear.

That's the story I heard from a former reporter of the *Reporter* and passed on to my crew. Like me, Tricia was pretty skeptical that there really was a ghost named Shoes who couldn't resist a nice slip-on or a pair of fancy boots. But, unlike me, Tricia tempted fate.

Our brush with footwear felony wasn't intentional. We had set out to try to find nobody again, without success. The 704 had just blown her whistle when we arrived at the first bench beyond the intersection of the trail and the paved access road. Tricia said she had a blister on her foot and sat down to remove her left tennis shoe. But as soon as she took it off, instead of removing her sock and inspecting her foot, she began to wave the shoe in the air. "Let's test out that shoe ghost," she said. Then she called out "Come and get it!" and dangled the sneaker in front of her, holding it by its shoestring. We all laughed. "Hey, Shoes! Where are you? Haven't you got any sole?" Again we burst out laughing. Well, not all of us.

"I wouldn't do that if I were you," Madame Lorraine warned her solemnly, but Tricia wasn't buying it. She was enjoying her little spectacle too much. "Hey, Shoes! Come 'n get it! Afraid I'll give you the boot?"

She looked so silly sitting on the bench, one shoe on and one off, that some of us were doubled over with laughter. Then I saw something that shocked me into silence. About twenty feet down the trail hovered something that looked like a heap of shoes about six feet tall. There were kid's

tennies and Mary Janes, men's work shoes and boat shoes, leather moccasins, spectators, golf shoes—even a pair of women's high heels! As I watched, the heap glided toward Tricia with surprising speed. Frozen in terror, she watched round-eyed as the shoe-thing stopped in front of the dangling shoe, as if

inspecting it carefully. Suddenly the shoe—and I am not making this up!—pulled itself from Tricia's grasp and began to float toward the shoe-heap. Tricia took a swipe at the errant sneaker but missed. The shoe hung suspended for a moment or two, then vanished so quickly that I cried out in astonishment. The pile of footwear disappeared just as abruptly.

"Wha...what was that?" Tricia said in alarm.

"That," Madame Lorraine said with a grin, "was Shoes. You and your sneaker have just had the privilege of becoming his latest victims."

MADAME LORRAINE'S SUGGESTION: *When passing by Shoe's favorite bench, greet the phantom (whether he's visible or not) with these words, "Nice shoes." This will help restore his self-respect, reduce his desire for revenge, and eventually help him to move toward the light.*

ORANGE FACE
DOWN

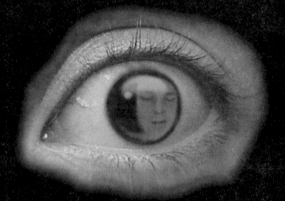

ORANGE FACE DOWN

NAME: *Albert Longfellow*

LOCATION: *Anywhere in the waters of Blacklick Creek*

MANIFESTATIONS: *Most often manifests as the reflection of a man's orange-colored face upside-down in still water.*

WARNING: *Do not enter the waters of the creek in order to examine this apparition.*

It's amazing how much interest my father has in ghosts, especially when you consider that he doesn't believe in them. The story of Albert K. Longfellow is a result of my father's investigation into the world of spirits at the local tavern. No pun intended.

My father set up an appointment for me to meet with a Mr. Todd K. Longfellow at Bar J. R. in Nanty-Glo. It seemed that Mr. Longfellow had a case for me to solve, one involving a ghost and a murder. I informed the crew that I was on to another ghost story and would not be joining them for meatless stew cooked over an open fire. When they learned that my "research" was taking place at Bar J.R., they decided to join me for an evening out.

We arrived at the humble establishment around 8:00 o'clock. My father was sitting at the bar with a thin man whose long, gray-streaked brown hair flowed down to the middle of his back. My father motioned for me to join them.

"This is my daughter, the ghost private eye," my father said, giving me a hug. "She'll solve this mystery for you."

"Mr. Todd Longfellow," the man said as he stood up. He gave me a snaggle-toothed grin and a firm handshake. He was the tallest, thinnest man I had ever met. I guessed he was pushing seven feet tall.

"Any relation to the poet?" I asked.

He peered at me as if I had sprouted an extra head. "Naw, I don't read much poetry," he said. "Say, you are a little one," he observed, referring to my slight build and modest stature. "But good things come in little packages, right, Daddy-boy?" He gave my dad a friendly, male-bonding-style punch in the gut. My dad agreed with him, but not in words; he answered Longfellow with a brotherly slap on the back. We decided to move to a booth, concluding that it would be a more comfortable place to conduct our business. My father informed me that if I paid for the drinks and a good meal I'd get a really exciting story.

As we passed by the pool table, where my crew was already into a game, the barkeeper was delivering them a pitcher of beer and three frosty mugs. I overheard Joe order a pizza with everything but anchovies. It sounded so good that I ordered a plain cheese pizza for myself.

"Make that a large, half with everything," Longfellow told the barkeep. "And bring an order of Buffalo wings and don't scrimp on the hot sauce, neither. And a boilermaker while you're at it, and you might as well throw in some French fries and a platter of those deep-fried mushrooms."

"Would you like anything else?" I asked Longfellow.

My sarcasm was lost on him. "Well, since you're buyin', how about a pitcher of beer? And a pound of steamed shrimp."

"Is that all for you, Mr. Longfellow?" I asked. "Or are you going to share it?"

"Well, I haven't had dinner yet. 'Course, we can share the beer. Go ahead and order whatever you want."

He sure is generous with other people's money, I thought. "I have a pizza coming, remember? Dad, would you like anything?" I smiled a wide, happy-face smile that signaled to my father that he was in big trouble if Longfellow's story wasn't a humdinger.

My dad ordered a shrimp basket, double fries and his own boilermaker, which was a shot of whiskey and a beer. When the food arrived, Longfellow launched himself at it like a heat-seeking missile. He appeared to enjoy his free banquet, barely pausing to utter a word except to ask for the ketchup or salt. As he wolfed down his food, he reminded me of some starving giant in a fairy tale.

I ended up with two slices of my own pizza and half a glass of beer.

"Well, Mr. Longfellow," I asked, once he appeared to be slowing down, "if there's nothing more you would like from the menu, perhaps you could tell me your story. It's getting late and I have to get up early."

"Wait. I haven't had dessert yet," he said, motioning to the barkeeper. "It would ruin a great dinner like this to not have dessert."

I agreed, and we all ordered coffee and a slice of pie. Or pies, in Longfellow's case. He had one slice each of blueberry, apple, peach and cherry, and would have had lemon meringue too except they had just sold the last piece.

"I'll be ready to tell my story in a few minutes," he said, instructing the barkeeper to bring his usual. I was quite surprised to learn that his usual after-dinner drink was a 1982 port from Portugal. I ordered one for myself. It seemed that Mr. Longfellow and I had something in common.

"My sister-in-law Maureen killed my brother," he said in such a casual way that I found myself open to believing him. "And she got away with it, too. I'm not saying that my dear brother was an altar boy, 'cause he wasn't. He was a bit over-ly fond of good scotch whiskey. But that's no reason to kill a man, is it?"

My father and I both shook our heads.

"And," he continued, pausing to savor a sip of port, "I don't think you should kill a guy for beating his wife and kids once in

a while. After all, it wasn't like anyone ended up in the hospital or anything like that. Although," he admitted, scratching his head, "there was that time he broke a couple ribs on his son, little Patrick, but my brother was only trying to discipline the boy. Can't blame a man for trying to teach a kid good manners, can you?"

My dad and I remained speechless.

"Did I mention that Albert was my twin?" Longfellow asked. "Yep, identical in almost every way, except he's dead and I'm not. And I never had much use for running around with the ladies like Albert. I been married for nearly forty-five years to the same woman. Never was unfaithful. Now Albert, he had a lot of wild oats to sow, but every time he sowed one he admitted to being the daddy. And he always gave the woman as much money as he could muster, although working in the mines off and on the way he did, he hardly had much to spare.

"That's why Maureen, pregnant or not—she mostly always had something in the oven—had to clean houses to make ends meet. And they probably would have met, too, if Albert hadn't borrowed the money from the sugar jar to spend on scotch. But, like I said before, just 'cause a man enjoys his liquor is no reason to kill him."

I stared at Longfellow, both amazed and amused. He reasoning was almost childlike in its contradictions. I had to get to the bottom of the story before Longfellow ordered another glass of port.

"Mr. Longfellow, exactly how did Maureen kill your brother Albert?" I guessed that she accidentally smacked him too hard over the head with an iron skillet. I couldn't help but think that if I were married to Albert Longfellow, I might be tempted to swing a heavy object in his direction too.

"She loosened a board on the bridge. Railroad trestle, to be exact."

All right, I thought to myself. This story isn't going anywhere. But I figured I might as well hear the whole thing. After all, I'd come this far and spent quite a lot of money. "You seem to be very certain."

"Yeah, I am. Maureen knew Al would be crossing the bridge that evening."

"How did she know?" my father asked. He was very much into the story. I could almost see the gears of his mind turning. He had a mystery to solve.

"'Cause he crossed it every evening on his way home from the bar. Knew every part of that trestle like he knew the back of his hand. That's the truth. He could walk across it drunk as a skunk, in the middle of the night, with his eyes closed, hopping on one foot. I know, because I saw him do it. I was getting pretty good at crossing it myself and I'd show you right now except they tore that bridge down shortly after my brother died. Accident, they called it." Suddenly his demeanor changed. His eyes flew open wide and he pounded the table with his fist. "Accident, my foot," he yelled. "It was murder!"

"You guys okay over there?" Joe called as he rosined his cuestick. I was moved by his concern.

"Don't let Todd get you all frazzled," the barkeeper said, waving his finger at Longfellow. "Now you quiet down, buddy, or you're going to have to leave. He gets like this whenever he's had too much to drink. I'll pour some coffee into him and make sure he gets home all right. You know, Todd, your wife is going to let you have it."

Todd brushed off the barkeeper's comments with a shrug of his shoulders. "Like I was saying," he continued, in a slightly steadier voice, "she killed him. I know 'cause I saw her on the bridge that day and she was bending down, working at something. I think she was pulling up boards, making a hole for Albert to trip over. Later I got to take a good look at the bridge deck, and sure enough you could see that a board had been pried up, exposing fresh wood. Anyway, whatever happened, the next thing I know, my brother's dead. It was an awful sight, indeed. He was hanging from the trestle, both feet caught between the planks. Drowned to death, he did."

"How did he drown?"

"As you can guess, he was tall, very tall, like me. Any other man would have slipped right through the hole in the bridge and into the water, but Al's big feet got caught. Size 14. Just like mine. Custom-made shoes." He pointed to his huge feet, encased in the largest tennis shoes I'd ever seen. "Anyhow, the water was six feet below the trestle. Al was six nine. I found him the next day, dangling from the bridge, his head submerged in the orange water of Blacklick Creek."

"Wait a second," I said, holding up my hand like a policeman stopping traffic. "Your brother was Orange Face Down?" Everybody in Twin Rocks knew Orange Face Down. Except for Maggie, he'd been sighted more often than any other ghost on the trail. "Why didn't you say so?"

"Damn, I hate it when people call him that!" Longfellow clenched his teeth. "But I hate it even more that people just brush off his death like some garden-variety accident. But tell me this, Miss Smarty-pants Ghostbuster, if it was an accident, why is my brother's spirit still walking the earth?"

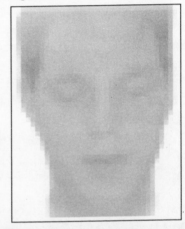

I pursed my lips and tapped one finger on the checkered tablecloth. That was a good point. As I have said before, ghosts normally have a reason for hanging around. Maybe Albert Longfellow had been the victim of foul play. We had received at least a hundred reports every summer since the trail opened describing the head of a man, floating just beneath the surface of the creek. His face was always brilliant orange. Chelley had taken several pictures of his long, colorful visage just beneath the surface of the

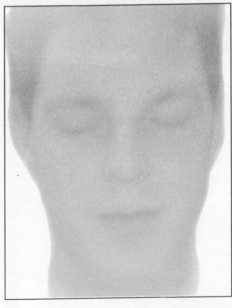

waters of Sulfur Creek. Now, thanks to my father, we knew who he was. Was Orange Face trying to tell us something?

I promised Longfellow that I would look into his brother's death. This, I believed, was another case for Madame Lorraine, and I was pretty sure that my involvement had pretty much come to an end. Then Mr. Longfellow informed me that Albert's wife, Maureen, was still alive and living in a local retirement village.

"I hear she's close to death's door," Longfellow went on. "Cancer, you know. Could go at any time. Being a good Christian woman, an Irish Catholic to boot, I'll bet she's willing to confess her crime, especially now since you can contact Al and get the whole story anyway." Mr. Longfellow sipped quietly from his mug of coffee. I studied him for a moment. He loved his brother, this much I could tell, and he was hell-bent on getting justice for his him.

"You know what this coffee needs?" he said, smacking his lips. "A shot of whiskey."

My father drove Mr. Longfellow home that night. My Dad told me that Mrs. Longfellow was waiting at the door for him and wasn't angry at him, not one bit, just relieved that he had made it home all right. They both seemed like decent people, despite Mister's fondess for food and drink.

The next day, I drove to Towering Pines Retirement Village and visited Maureen Longfellow, an endearing Irish lady in her seventies who had a private room in the infirmary. She was having a good day, and was able to sit up in a wheelchair and join me in a cup of tea and a plate of shortbread cookies. Maureen's gray-green eyes brightened when I mentioned her husband, and she was more than happy to talk about him. Not the usual modus operandi of a murderess, but hey! She was Irish. Her people were born storytellers.

"Oh, Albert. A fine man he was," she said, taking a sip of tea. The porcelain cup found a precarious harbor in her gnarled, trembling hands. "I miss him so, even to this day. And that's not to say that he didn't have a temper on him, aye, and could deal a blow with the best of them, especially if he'd had a drop of the Craetur in him."

"The crater?" All I could think of was lunar landscapes.

"Whiskey to you, love," Maureen said. She had such a lush, lilting accent that I could have listened to her all day and all night, even if she did nothing more than read the phone book. "Poor Albert did have that failing, he did, like many men before him, better and worse. Aye, there was many a green dollar that went into the till at the Rover's Bar and Grill that should have gone to feeding and keeping our ten darlin' wee boys."

I closed one eye. Did I detect a little resentment? Maureen seemed to read my mind. "Not that I begrudged Albert his fun, mind you," she went on, breaking a piece of shortbread into manageable morsels. "He worked hard in the mines for every dollar he ever earned, bless him. And if he sometimes borrowed a little of my own cash that I'd set aside for the boys, well, I didn't mind. He always swore he'd pay me back, and I'm sure he would have, if he'd lived, poor man." Maureen sniffed and dabbed at her eyes with a linen handkerchief.

Was she sincere? She seemed to be. Still, I decided in the interests of justice to press her a little bit. "I'm sorry to bring this up," I said, "but there have been reports about, well, other women in Albert's life."

"Oh, aye, he was quite the lady's man, my husband." Her rose-tinted cheeks grew a deeper shade of pink. "That's a common failing among the gentlemen as well," she said, with an air of philosophical detachment. "I never doubted that he'd stay with me, but I don't mind saying that it was a little hard, watching him spend money on gifts for the ladies when the lads went without." She was silent a moment, and I wondered just how deeply this woman had been hurt. Then she was off again, making excuses for the man. "They say that some men have greater needs than others, if you understand my meaning. Now it must be said in his favor that he never brought them around to the house, and he was most discreet around the townsfolk. That's a great comfort, you know, to save face in front of one's friends."

"Yes, of course," I said, but I knew from having lived in Twin Rocks that everybody knew everybody else's business. It was just a fact of life in a small town. You couldn't hide a mistress there any more than you could hide an elephant in Bar J.R., and Maureen must have known this. "Your children must have been a great comfort to you as well."

A beatific smile burst out over her wrinkled face. "Indeed they were, and still are," she said. "I have my nine boys yet, and fine lads they are, each of them married to a lovely lass. And I have twenty-three grandchildren. Think on that, now. Twenty-three! And two more on the way. Ah, isn't that grand!" Maureen filled her teacup, her hands shaking so badly that I almost reached out to help her. But I resisted, and I was glad I did. She was an independent old gal.

"Still, it was a great sadness about dear little Patrick, my youngest," she said softly. From the way she spoke I knew at once that the child had died. "He was only nine years old when the angels came for him. A terrible tragic accident it was."

I remembered what Todd had said about Patrick, that Albert had injured him, and I decided to question Maureen a little further. "Forgive me, but I'll need the details for my book. How did Patrick die?"

A wary gleam appeared in the old woman's eyes. "Poor love. A fall from a pony. A neighbor's pony, it was, frightened by a dog. The worst luck I've every had, let me assure you." A tear ran down her withered cheek, and she blotted her face with a paper napkin.

"I'm so sorry," I said. I considered bringing up Todd's remark about Albert's method of 'discipline', then decided against it. Why go out of my way to bring grief to a dying woman? "Again, please excuse me, but there's something I feel I must ask you. Todd Longfellow, Albert's twin brother, has said he thought he saw you on the bridge the day before Albert died, pulling up boards. I was just wondering how you reacted to that accusation…not that I believe it, of course."

Maureen dunked a piece of shortbread into her tea; she was imperturbable. "Well, lass, I've heard his blather before. Of course there's no truth in it, and no one in town put any store in it. Todd's a good lad, but he's over-fond of the drink, you know, just like his brother. Why would I even think of harming Albert? I loved him, and I depended on him, too. Aye, we had our share of troubles, but what couple doesn't?"

We spoke about other things for a few minutes, then I tried to test her one more time; either she was a nice, genuine lady or she was a good liar. "You must feel pretty isolated living here," I began. "For example, it must be hard getting to church and…getting to confession."

She wasn't fazed in the least. "Oh, I have no trouble at all that way," she said cheerily. "Father Matthew comes to see me at least twice a month."

Dead end, I thought. No way would a priest ever mention anything revealed during a confession. "How convenient for you," I replied.

Maureen smiled in such a way as to let me know that she hoped I was going to leave soon. "Did I tell you that my Donald's wife, Lisa, is bringing my grandson to visit me today? Justin's only three, but he's a darlin' little fellow and as smart as a whip."

I caught on to her cue. "I'm sure he is. Well, I won't take up any more of your time. You must be quite tired, and I should be getting back to my crew. Thanks so much for your time and for being so forthcoming with me."

After we made our good-byes, a nurse escorted me to the front entrance of the infirmary. On my way to the parking lot, I saw an attractive woman with a sweet little boy walking down the path I had just taken. Little Justin, I thought, and suddenly I didn't care whether the old lady had killed her husband or not. That was long ago, and now Maureen's time on earth was almost up. She was surrounded by people who loved her, as she deserved to be. Did she do it? I wasn't sure. Albert might not have deserved to die, but he certainly wasn't a good husband or father. Since the town had been satisfied with Maureen's story, then I guess I could be too. Todd would just have to continue living with his doubts.

Back at camp, I told Madame Lorraine about my visit with the delightful Mrs. Albert Longfellow. "How much research did you do on this case?" she asked.

"Not much," I admitted. In fact, I hadn't done anything except listen to Todd's and Maureen's sides of the story. "But I've decided just to let sleeping Orange Face Downs lie. Even if Maureen were accused of Albert's murder, she'd be dead before the trial would be finished. Personally, I can't tell whether she's lying or not."

"Well, of course she is," Madame said softly, adjusting the silk scarf around her neck. "She killed him."

"What?"

Madame Lorraine held a finger up to her lips, signaling that she was speaking to me in strictest confidence. "I had contact with Albert. He said Maureen came up to him while he was thrashing in the water, but ignored his cries for help. But there's something else you should know. Didn't Maureen say that Patrick died in a fall?"

"Right," I said, still a little dazed at her news. "From a neighbor's pony."

Madame smiled indulgently. "The Irish are so imaginative. Miss Cynthia, these were coal-mining folk. They couldn't afford a pet pony. Did you know that Patrick died from a broken rib that punctured his heart?"

Broken rib. The image sounded familiar. "Todd said that Albert cracked Patrick's ribs once."

"He was being evasive, or maybe protective. Maybe he had forced himself to forget the truth, which was that Albert struck the boy's ribs with such force that he drove one of them into the child's heart. People outside the house could hear the bones snapping. If you were a mother whose husband killed your child, what would you do?"

There wasn't the ghost of a doubt in my mind how I'd react in that kind of situation. And I'm sure there hadn't been in Maureen's mind, either. "I'd kill the bastard the first chance I got."

"Case closed," Madame Lorraine said. "This is another ghost who deserves to linger in twilight for some time to come."

DRIVEN TO
DEATH

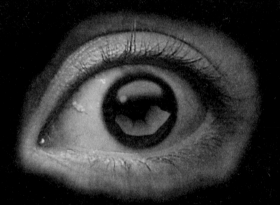

DRIVEN TO DEATH

NAMES: *Ron Celestine, Doodles Howard, Mark Napoli, Gabe Slodjski, Carol Friendly and Betsy Fleer*

LOCATION: *Anywhere on the trail from Twin Rocks to Vintondale.*

MANIFESTATIONS: *Mostly body parts and pieces. Complete, vivid apparitions are very rare and may include grotesque combinations of body parts.*

WARNING: *Since the body parts are interchangeable, it is very strongly suggested that you don't try to pick up or tamper with any of the pieces. They may get mixed up with your own.*

The day Ron Celestine turned sixteen years old two major incidents in his life occurred: The first was, he got his driver's license. The second was, he died. He didn't die alone, though. He took five other kids with him, three boys and two girls. There's a saying that you shouldn't drive any faster than your guardian angel can fly. Unfortunately for my friends, R. C. exceeded his angel's speed limit.

The accident was a gruesome, bloody mess. All those body pieces scattered on the pavement, along side the road, in the bushes, hanging from the trees, not to mention the foot they found in Miss Bevory's mailbox. Like I said, it was awful. I am just thankful that I missed my ride to my high school football game that night or I would, at this very moment, be on the Ghost Town Trail, trying to get it together. Literally.

The newspaper reported the accident as another disaster involving an inexperienced driver going too fast, but I knew that more was involved. R. C. was driving 120 miles an hour down Breakneck Hill because it was what all the kids in the area did when they got their license. You tried to beat the hill. The plan was to go down Breakneck at "breakneck" speed so the momentum would carry the car up the next hill. R.C didn't make it. A lot of kids didn't. They only difference was that their cars didn't explode into a million pieces.

A couple of years ago, local police began receiving reports that people were finding body parts on the trail—fingers, eyes, ears and an occasional leg. When the police came to investigate, they didn't find a thing. At first they thought some wild animal had dragged the remains away, but they finally concluded that the parts weren't real. They figured that some prankster was using plastic replicas of limbs and organs to scare the visitors on the trail.

But, when reports of five ghostly mismatched teenagers started to trickle in, I decided to investigate, even though I really didn't want to. I had a sneaking suspicion that I personally knew these ghosts and I was bound by friendship to try to help them.

"We're searching for some nasty-looking ghosts," I informed the crew one morning. "They've been in a terrible accident. You may see a girl's body with a guy's head, or someone with a leg where an arm should be. Try to remain calm. Get a picture and leave the rest up to me and Madame Lorraine."

"Damn straight we will," Joe said. "I have a big enough problem sorting out my own life."

We all chuckled. It is always best to go into these things with a sense of humor.

We didn't have long to wait. Early that afternoon, around one o'clock, we saw a phantom finger lying underneath a bench. It wiggled like a fat white worm for a few seconds, then vanished. Chelley didn't have time to get it on film.

I called out the names of Ron, Betsy, Carol, Doodles, Mark and Gabe, my friends who perished. I repeated them several times as we walked along the trail. My efforts paid off. About two miles in from the trail's head, I saw all six of them standing beside the path, looking as if they had been traced on the air in very faint pencilstrokes. Although they did not acknowledge my presence or respond in any way to us, I somehow knew that I had made a connection with them. They kept glancing around, as if they expected to see someone watching them.

"Quick! Set up the equipment!" I shouted. The crew looked at me as if I were nuts.

"Why? Do you see something?" Chelley asked.

I realized then that only I could discern my ghostly high school chums. "Yes. Just set up the equipment and aim it in the direction I'm pointing. And be sure to take pictures!"

As the crew began setting up, the meters on the infrared-sensing equipment went wild, vacillating back and forth like an infant's suction toy on a spring. "Something's out there for sure," Joe whispered.

"I wish you could see them too," I said. I gazed in sad astonishment as the youthful specters exchanged arms, legs, noses and teeth with each other as they tried to get themselves back together. If the scene hadn't been so tragic, I would have thought I was watching a cartoon.

The phantoms vanished a few minutes after they had arrived. I called Madame Lorraine from my cell phone and described to her the odd spectacle I had just witnessed. "I'm afraid that there is nothing that can be done today to help your friends," she said. "I am quite familiar with their story, although I have never communicated with them personally. My spirit guide has told me this much: They are afraid to face their parents with the 'mess' they have created, so they're trying to put the pieces back together themselves before trying to tell Mom and Dad what happened."

"Do you mean to say that they don't know they're dead?" I asked, hardly believing that they could not know.

"Well, yes," she replied. "They're so worried about what their parents will say about ruining the car and mangling their bodies that death is of little concern to them."

"So, what do we do to help?" I trusted Madame Lorraine would certainly have a solution.

"Unfortunately, Miss Cynthia, these young people are caught in their last thought, like a fly preserved in amber."

"What thought might that be?" I asked.

"Mom and Dad are gonna kill me."

Madame Lorraine explained that releasing my friends from this worldly plane would be very difficult if not impossible because it required the involvement of so many people. She further explained that the parents of the dead teenagers had to be willing to somehow communicate to their lost children that making mistakes is a part of growing up, that no matter what they did, they would never lose the love of their parents.

Trying to convince six sets of parents that their dead kids needed their help was going to be a tough assignment for me. I knew right off the bat that Doodles' mother was never going to buy into any idea that originated with me. From first grade on, Doodles's mom was convinced that I was the strangest kid in school. Once she told me I "wouldn't amount to a hill of beans." My career as a ghostologist would be the final piece of evidence to let her rest her case.

Then there was Betsy's dad. Because I was late meeting up with R. C., Betsy had taken my place on that fatal drive. Although he never directly blamed me for his daughter's death, Betsy's dad did say at the funeral that I should learn to be on time.

I thanked Madame Lorraine for her suggestion and placed my cell phone in my backpack. There had to be another way. Eventually, I knew, I would find it.

DRIVING BLIND

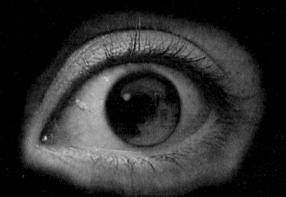

DRIVING BLIND

NAMES: *Billy Platman, Bobby Harton*

LOCATION: *Anywhere on the trail from Twin Rocks to Vintondale*

MANIFESTATIONS: *Random hikers have seen two spectral young men walking together, engrossed in conversation. They are never seen apart.*

WARNING: *Do not disturb or try to make contact with these two spirits. See Madame Lorraine's comments at the end of this section.*

I learned two things early on. One: A person can only handle so much grief before a little defensive mechanism kicks in, locking it away for another time. Two: You don't have to be driving fast or recklessly to get killed in a car crash.

The encounter on the trail with my six dead buddies who died trying to conquer Breakneck Hill triggered a memory that I had kept buried for a long time. It was the "murders" of Billy Platman and Bobby Harton. They lost their lives about three weeks after Ron crashed his car on the very same highway. I don't remember the details of their funerals, but I do remember feeling enraged about the circumstances of their deaths.

Over the years, I had heard stories about two teenage ghosts walking the trail, their arms around each other's necks, lost in conversation that only they can hear. The young men are around sixteen or seventeen years old and fit the descriptions of Billy and Bobby. At first I chose to ignore these reports, but during the last twenty-four hours on the trail, I knew that the time had come for me to unlock a door that I had slammed shut many years ago.

After dinner, I asked Joe to take a walk with me. As we strolled down the trail toward Twin Rocks, I told him the story of my friends.

"Those boys that everyone sees on the trail," I said. "Well, they're two of my chums from high school, Billy and Bobby."

"Wow!" Joe raised his head a little, but it was getting pretty hard to shock him. "You sure know a lot of ghosts!"

"Yes, but these two were special," I went on. "They were inseparable since the day they met in the first grade. Remember when you and I got lost in the Mohave? That was when we forged the same kind of bond that Billy and Bobby had for most of their lives."

Joe laughed, exposing the spaces between his front teeth. If it weren't for those gaps, he would have been a handsome man. Joe understood the kind of friendship I was referring to, the kind that is instant and permanent, just as if two people had been cemented together with Crazy Glue.

"They really complemented each other, like you and I." I gave him a friendly swat on the arm. "Billy had a physical, joyful sense of humor, like a clown at a circus, and he was just as outgoing. Bobby was more on the quiet side but always laughed heartily at his buddy's jokes. Bobby was unusually bright, near genius I'd say. Billy was average, but a talented swimmer and track runner. Our algebra teacher was right when he said that Billy and Bobby were two halves who together completed one whole person.

"Billy and Bobby had taken their driver's test the same day. Bobby passed. Billy, however, parked the car in drive; when he got out, the old Dodge drifted across the lane and smacked into a bus. Fortunately for him, no one was hurt. Fortunately for all of us, he didn't get his license."

"There's a story a'brewing here, right?"

"You bet," I said, "and a sad one, too. Listen up. The boys bought a 1954 Ford Fairlane from the money they had earned delivering papers and doing odds jobs for their neighbors. They worked hard all summer painting the entire car, patching the torn leather upholstery and polishing the rusted chrome bumpers. The final touch: a St. Christopher medal on the dash. After that, they were ready to take the Ford out for its maiden voyage.

"Their first objective was to pick up their girlfriends, Joy and Julie Barnhart, twin sisters. I can't remember who liked whom, but somehow it seemed fitting that those two boys were in love with basically the same girl. I saw them that night at the movie theater. They were sitting directly in front of me and Tom. (We hadn't gotten married yet.) All six of us chatted for a few minutes before the movie started, and I gave Billy some of my Boston Baked Beans. Afterwards, Billy asked if we wanted to go grab a burger with him and the others, but Tom and I declined.

"The next morning I learned that Billy and Bobby had been killed. The news devastated me. Eight of my friends dead within a few weeks, which worked out to be one-fifth of my high school class: It's a wonder I didn't need psychological treatment. It was my saving grace that I had an understanding mother and father whom I could talk to about my feelings.

"As I said, Billy and Bobby's deaths weren't really an accident. They were more like murder or manslaughter, which made the whole situation that much more horrendous to me. Two guys home from college were celebrating a family wedding when they decided to go out for a joy ride. Not quite drunk but close, they left the reception hall located in Ebensburg at a few minutes to midnight in their dad's Lincoln Towne Car. Like so many others before them, they drove at high speed up Breakneck Hill, and when they came to a level stretch on the highway, they decided to turn their lights off and drive blind. A dangerous and foolish stunt, it was the preferred method for bone-headed boys of that era to prove their manhood.

"At midnight, Billy and Bobby said goodnight to Joy and Julie and were on their way home. Bobby stopped at the intersection of Cardiff Road and Route 422, then pulled out on the highway. The Lincoln hit them broadside traveling fifty miles an hour. I'm sure neither of them knew what struck them. Their old car skidded across the highway and slammed into a brick building. Each instantly died from a broken neck.

"The two brothers who were driving blind ran from the scene of the accident. When the police found them hours later, they were huddled together, crying in a drain ditch less then a quarter of a mile from the accident. They didn't even have so much as a bloody nose or one black and blue mark. The day they buried Billy and Bobby, the boys who killed them were on their way back to college. Today, the oldest brother is a high-profile political figure in Harrisburg, and the younger one, a lawyer, works in the family's real estate development company in Ebensburg."

"I guess Daddy must have pulled some strings," Joe said.

"Oh, yeah, very big strings," I answered grimly. "He was a very influential man."

"You know how I would handle this?" Joe continued. "I would do it alone. You don't need any of us to help you on this one. Call those two brothers and get their side of the story. Let 'em know that you're investigating the sightings of Billy and Bobby's ghosts and are going to write a story about them. That should shake 'em up."

"You're right. I'll do it tomorrow."

"First thing," he said sternly.

"First thing," I promised. The more I thought about Joe's suggestion, the more I agreed with him. By talking about what happened that night, openly and honestly, perhaps we all might be able to find a way to escape a past that haunted us.

I called the oldest brother first. He declined my request for an interview. The younger one, however, agreed, so long as I kept his name a secret. We agreed on an alias—Mr. Doe.

We met in his office, which was located in the most affluent part of town. His inner sanctum was spacious and decorated with antique hunting prints and bronze statuary, as I suspected it would be. As I sat in an overstuffed, burgundy leather chair waiting for Mr. Doe, I noticed an art deco silver frame with a picture of two young boys on the credenza behind his desk. Beside it was a picture of an attractive woman who I assumed was his wife. As I looked about the room, I must admit I felt a surge of resentment building up inside of me for a man I had never met.

When Mr. Doe enter in the room I was surprised at his slight appearance. He was only a few years old than me but looked haggard, almost sickly. His sandy-colored hair was closely cropped and he wore an earring in his left ear—quite a rebellious statement in these parts. Maybe the woman was his sister, I thought.

He politely asked me if I wanted something to drink. I politely declined.

"Well," he said with an air of resignation, "We both know why you're here, don't we? To save us both time, let me tell you about my crime and punishment. I think you wouldn't have many questions for me after that."

I took out my tape recorder and turned it on, but he immediately motioned for me to shut it off. "You may take notes." He handed me a pen and a legal tablet. "Of course, you know, Cynthia, that it will always be my word against yours. And frankly, I'm a wealthy attorney and you...."

"Are not," I said, finishing his sentence for him. I knew he was alluding to me being a ghostologist, but I didn't want to give him the opportunity to insult the profession.

"That wasn't quite the point I was going to make," he said with a laugh. "Actually, you may do better than me someday. You never can tell." He sank into his hunter green plush chair, which I assumed was custom made, and settled down behind his desk.

"Beautiful piece of furniture," I said, tapping the gleaming wood.

"Eighteenth century Italian," he noted, without emotion. "Cost a fortune. Can't say it's brought me much happiness." For a while we sat in silence, and I was about to ask him if he'd changed his mind when he resumed speaking. "I know this isn't any sort of proper excuse," he said, "but I was young and stupid. My brother and I both were. We never thought for one moment that anyone would get hurt, much less killed.

"I wasn't the one driving, you know. My brother Nate was. It was my father's idea for me to take the rap for Nate, who was in his senior year at Penn State. Dad didn't want anything to interfere with Nate's graduation, so he talked me into taking the blame. And believe me, over the years I have paid the price for Billy and Bobby's death. I've been my own judge and jury, and

I've sentenced myself to a life of pain. Don't think I haven't suffered plenty for my crime, both physically and emotionally."

I didn't know what to say, but Mr. Doe wasn't finished. He stretched his hand across his elegant desk and gently stroked the two photographs. "Yes, I have everything, right? A million-dollar house, a yacht, more luxury cars than a man should have…plus a beautiful wife and two great kids. Thing is, it's all a lie. I'm never home, I get seasick, I've been caught DUI so often I've lost my license, and Dad bought my family. That's right, he bought it. Susan married me for the money, knowing full well that we wouldn't have any real life together. We each have our own separate existence, except for special functions and photo opportunities.

"And the boys? Poor kids. Dad arranged for us to adopt them from an orphanage in Calcutta, but frankly they would have had a happier life if they'd stayed in India. It's not that I don't like them, I just never spent enough time to get to know them. They're in boarding school now, and the only time they're part of the 'family' is when we need them as props in publicity photos."

He slouched back in his chair, sighing. Such a sick, bitter man, I thought. Which was the better fate? To live a happy life and die instantly in an accident, like Billy and Bobby, or to suffer a living death, like Mr. Doe? The answer was obvious. "Did you know that the spirits of those boys you killed are still here, haunting the Ghost Town Trail?" I said quietly. "And they're more than ghosts; they were my friends. I'd give anything if they could be released."

"What do you recommend?" he asked, folding his hands under his chin, as if he were praying.

"I don't know," I said. "I'm in touch with a skilled psychic, but her best advice is to do nothing. I was sort of hoping you'd be able to supply a solution…." My voice trailed off.

"I'm quite a disappointment, aren't I?" he said, with a forlorn smile. "To you and me both, I'd say. No, sorry, there's not much I can do in this state." Mr. Doe spread his arms wide, and for the first time I saw just how frail and emaciated he really was.

His expensive suit hung on him like the skin of a dead animal, and his face had the tight, angular look of someone who was battling for his life. "Do you know how many meds I take just to give me the strength to come into the office?"

I sensed his despair but said nothing. Once again, there was nothing to say.

After a while, he sat up, rested his arms on his desk and continued. "I know I'll never be able to help your ghost friends in this life, but, if there is a spirit world and I'm part of it, I swear I'll try to do something for them. I'm not saying I believe in ghosts, mind you, but you just never know, do you?"

On this point I agreed, and told him so.

A month after our meeting, I was sitting in my kitchen, leafing through my hometown newspaper that my mother dutifully sends me every week, when I came across a picture I recognized as a photo of Mr. Doe. It was accompanied by his obituary. While the official cause of death was listed as pneumonia, I knew that the real cause was probably something far less socially acceptable. Mr. Doe's dad had probably crossed more than a few hands with silver to keep the family name untarnished. I wasn't surprised to see that the lawyer had died, given his illness, but his death did make me think about his offer of unearthly assistance.

I half closed my eyes and, in my imagination, saw a third spirit, trailing after Billy and Bobby, calling out to get their attention and alert them to their fate. The more they ignored the new phantom, the louder it screamed and the faster it pursued them. Then the image disappeared, and I was sitting in my kitchen, clutching the obituary page.

Could such a thing happen? Could a dead man's guilt really force him to try to make amends with his victims? I knew better than to dwell on these questions. When it comes to ghosts, you just never know.

MADAME LORRAINE'S SUGGESTIONS: *Although it would be preferable if Billy and Bobby were able to accept their deaths, it does no harm to leave them exactly as they are. They are perfectly happy walking the trail,* sharing their dreams and ideas, and in all honesty these two "best buddies" probably don't even know that they are dead. In addition, it would pose significant danger to anyone uninitiated  in psychic communication to try to inform these boys of their deceased status. Spirits of the dead who gain abrupt self-awareness can exhibit erratic, even violent behavior. If it's true that the late Mr. Doe intends to enlighten Billy and Bobby, so much the better. After all, he owes them a favor.

THE TREE WHO
HUGGED BACK

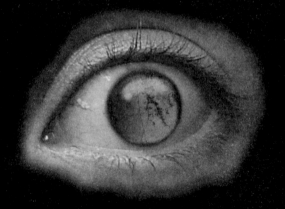

THE TREE
WHO HUGGED BACK

NAME: *Lenny Starsky*

LOCATION: *Secret*

MANIFESTATIONS: *None so far. Although it is too soon to tell, we suspect that Lenny Starsky has not yet passed over and may come to haunt the trail yet.*

helley had just finished packing the last of the camera equipment into a small wagon attached to her mountain bike. Our campsite was all but empty. Our three-week adventure on the Ghost Town Trail was nearly over. I was pondering what final words of wisdom I could give to the crew when I heard my father calling to me from the edge of the trail.

"What's wrong?" I ran toward him shouting. "Is everything all right?"

"You're not going to believe this, "he said, sucking in air. So many people start their conversations with me with those words. "They found Lenny Starsky dead near that oak tree you call Ajap. His wife reported him missing yesterday. The coroner's up there now. I passed his car on the way here." My father was obviously listening to the police scanner that he kept on top of the refrigerator.

"Who's Lenny Starsky?" I asked. My father was always assuming that, because he knew someone, I did, too.

"You know, Lenny Starsky. He owns the lumber mill. You met him when he clear-cut the woods near Uncle Raymond's place."

"Oh, yeah." I remembered Lenny all right. Our meeting was punctuated by a rather loud discussion on ecology and respect for the environment that was triggered by his "accidentally" cutting down a large cherry tree on my uncle's property. "How did he die?"

"Don't know. If you're lucky, a tree strangled him and bingo! You've got another story. Let's go check it out."

"I don't know, Dad. I have to get back to Pittsburgh tonight and we're already behind schedule...."

"What's a few minutes more?" he asked. Nothing, until they turn into hours, I thought. I told the crew I'd be back in an hour or two, then followed Dad to the parking lot and got into the car beside him. We drove off in search of another adventure, though I was fairly certain that we were on a wild ghost chase. We parked along side the road, behind a police cruiser. As I was getting out of my car, I saw my cousin, Detective Stan, walking toward the woods. "Hey, Handsome!" I called out to him.

He turned and glowered at me like a deer trying to stare down a Mac Truck. "You again!" he snapped. "I haven't seen you in ten years, now I see you twice in a matter of days. Go figure! And every time you show up, something goes wrong. Just like when we were kids."

"I love you, too," I shot back, but this time I didn't feel like bantering. "I hear Lenny Starsky died up there by the big oak," I said. "What happened?"

Stan shrugged. "I dunno. Just got here myself. Rumor has it that it's a suicide, but you didn't hear me say that."

I took a deep breath and decided then and there to make a ridiculously bold request. The worst Stan could do would be to turn me down. "Since the tree's going to be in my book, I need to record anything unusual that happens to it. I don't suppose you'd let me have a look around, huh?"

"No," he barked.

"Aw, please? For old times' sake?"

We argued back and forth a bit, him growling and me whining. At last he glared at me again, glanced at my dad, then gave one brief nod. "Okay, you come with me. I owe you one for the Wilderman kids. But don't touch a thing and don't do anything nutty like screaming or something. It could be pretty gruesome. " He turned to face my father. "Uncle Walt," he called, "Cindy'll be back very soon. Please wait here for her." Stan looked back at me. "God, I hope I don't regret this."

"I'm not going to get you into trouble, am I?" I puffed, hurrying after him as he strode off down a wooded trail. Instantly we were engulfed by dense forest. I guess I had forgotten how passionately I had begged to join him.

"Naw, I'm a captain. I can't break the rules, but I can sure tweak the hell out of 'em. Just don't cross onto any of the areas I mark off with yellow tape."

I promised.

Minutes later we came to the hillside where Ajap lived. The oak's leaves seemed to droop and its limbs appeared to bend down, as if weighted by some invisible source. A grease-stained chain saw lay nestled among the exposed roots at the base of the massive tree. The sharp scent of gasoline filled the air.

Stan pointed to one of Ajap's sentinels. "My God! Look at that!" he cried, his voice shaken by an uncharacteristic tremor of fear.

As we approached one of the smaller oaks, I saw Lenny Starsky's body suspended in the crushing grip of the tree's branches. I let out a cry of surprise at the twisted look of terror on Lenny's face. His bulging, blood-filled eyes stared straight ahead in the direction of Ajap. Lenny's mouth was stuffed with something that looked like ivy—shiny, green and attached to the ground by a long, thin vine.

"What happened? I whispered, not wanting to believe what was right in front of me.

"It's not really clear," said a voice behind me.

I jumped about a foot into the air and spun around. There stood Dr. Nicolletti, the county coroner, who was also the local undertaker as well as the major of Twin Rocks. In that part of the world, it wasn't uncommon for one person to wear many unlikely hats.

Dr. Nicolletti frowned and peered at me in suspicion. "Stan, who the devil is this? What's she doing here?"

Stan, still trembling from the hideous sight of Lenny's body, introduced me to the good doctor. "Dr. Nick, this is my cousin, Cindy, the famous ghostologic and psychic." The last he threw in for good measure, as I had never made any claims to psychic ability. "She's okay."

"If you say so," the doctor grumbled, clearly offended by my presence. "Maybe she can ask the spirit world what happened here."

"What's your take on it?" Stan asked.

"Here's the best I can come up with," Dr. Nicolletti said, waggling his head as if he were trying to clear it of unpleasant ideas. "Lenny was about to cut down that old oak tree over there when somebody jumped him. Come here, I'll show you something."

We went over to Ajap. I greeted the majestic tree with the ceremonial bow that my grandfather had taught. The doctor pointed to some marks on the ground where it appeared as if something or someone had been dragged. The marks led to the sentinel where Lenny was still hanging.

"Here's my theory," the doctor continued. "While Lenny was preparing to cut down the tree, some local youths spoiling for trouble overpowered him, strung him up in the tree and wrapped ivy around him as a practical joke, just to scare him, you know, a sort of "tree gets revenge" scenario. Unfortunately, the joke got out of hand and Lenny had a heart attack. Or choked on the vegetation. Only an autopsy can pinpoint the cause of death."

"Imaginative and plausible," I said. "But how do you explain the fact that there are no footprints here but ours and Lenny's?"

Stan, who had been busy stringing yellow tape around the area, came up beside me. "She's got a point, Doc. And look! There are no ropes, cables, wire, twine—nothing at all holding him up. Only tree branches, and they've got him in a bear hug."

Dr. Nicolletti crossed his arms over his chest in a defensive gesture. "Mind you, it's only a theory. Have either of you got a better explanation?"

"You know what I think?" I moved closer to Lenny, careful not to step over Stan's yellow barrier. "I think they were protecting Ajap."

"Who's Ajap and who are they? Stan demanded. "Wait a minute. Let me guess. Ajap is the big oak."

I nodded.

"But who is 'they'?"

"The other trees and the ivy."

"I'm not getting involved in this line of…speculation," the doctor sniffed with noticeable sarcasm. But he continued to listen to my hypothesis.

"See, they don't want to hurt anyone but they were desperate. They had to protect the spirit of Ajap who lives in the big oak, because he holds a piece of a great truth that could one day save…." I paused. My theory was beginning to sound stupid, even to me. But what other explanation was there? "…The world," I ended, lamely.

"Wait a second. This all sounds vaguely familiar to me," Stan said. His eyes flicked over the landscape left to right, back and forth, as if he were searching for something. "Grandpa Mike's story. I remember the night he told us about those trees. You still believe that stuff?"

I had to admit that I kind of still did. Not all of it, of course, but a lot of it. Some of it, anyway.

"Remind me never to consider going into business with you," Stan said. With a snort and a shake of his head, he dismissed my theory as sheer rubbish. "Here's my theory," he began. "Lenny was out here alone doing what he does best—cutting down trees—when he was suddenly so overcome with remorse that he talked himself into taking his own life. He climbed a tree in order to hang himself, but slipped and fell into the branches. "

"Works for me," Dr. Nicolletti muttered. "Pending my examination, of course."

"What?" I stared at the two of them in disbelief. "Stan, you know that Len Starsky never had a remorseful day in his life. And any fool can see that he's not just tangled in those branches. They're smashing him against the trunk like a praying mantis crushing a fly. You said so yourself!"

Stan was mumbling something in a vain attempt to reinforce his position when the sentinel tree emitted a loud shriek, as piercing as the cry of a tortured soul. All three of us turned to stare at Lenny's body. Suddenly the limbs of the oak, which were twisted back in on the trunk, straightened out, just like a man stretching his arms. This movement released the corpse, which toppled to the ground and came to rest several yards from the tree.

For a moment we all stood frozen in place. I can't remember what was going through my mind. It was as if I lost touch with my surroundings for a moment. "Did you see that?" I whispered to Stan.

He nodded. "He fell out of the tree," he said, his voice calm but his face fixed in terror.

"Only after the tree released him!" I shouted, forgetting my promise not to do anything "nutty." "That tree moved its arms! You saw it, I saw it, Dr. Nicolletti saw it. We all heard the scream, too."

Neither of them contradicted me; in fact, they said nothing, just stared at the twisted body at the base of the tree, almost as if they were in a trance. When they finally came to themselves, the three of us trotted over to Lenny's corpse. His neck was broken in the fall and his head lay in an ungodly position under his arm.

"Look here," the coroner said, pointing to Lenny's midriff. A strand of ivy poked through Lenny's plaid shirt. Dr. Nicolletti took a few pictures, then straightened the body and unbuttoned the shirt. "Holy God Almighty!" he said, jumping away in fright. A gaping hole in Lenny's stomach revealed a horrific sight: his entire belly was stuffed with ivy.

"How in the…?" Stan began, but stopped abruptly. He stared at me speechless. He coughed, clearing his voice. "Ajap?" he whispered.

"Ajap?" I returned the question.

I stayed around and watched as they bagged Lenny. It wasn't a pretty sight. As Dr. Nicolletti shoved Lenny's arm in the bag, he made another gruesome discovery. On the inside of Lenny's left wrist, just beneath the thin outer layer of skin, was a tiny leaf.

"How did that get there?" I wondered out loud. I felt myself getting sick.

Dr. Nicolletti didn't answer right away. His eyes moved slowly from left to right and I could tell he was searching for an answer that would ease our minds. Finally he came up with one. "This is not a leaf. It's only an odd vein formation. Happens all the time."

"Oh, okay," Stan and I blurted out at the same time. Neither of us had any problem with the good doctor's most reasonable explanation.

"You gonna have a problem staying here by yourself?" I asked Stan, as I steadied the gurney that the doctor had brought with him.

"Nope," he answered, as he and the doctor hoisted Lenny's body onto the wheeled cot. "There's nothing to be afraid of." I didn't know whether he was saying that for my benefit or his.

"You've always been very brave," I whispered into Stan's ear as I hugged him good-bye. "Stupid, but brave."

As I helped Dr. Nicolletti maneuver the gurney down the sloping terrain, I briefly glanced back at Stan. He had wasted no time in getting down to the business of gathering clues. I was almost certain that they would never 'find' Lenny's killer but I was darn sure that at least three people knew who the killer was.

We almost lost Lenny when the gurney tipped over onto its side. It was good thing he was strapped on tight. It was a struggle to right the thing but we managed. I noticed that the bag had a small tear in it and that one of Lenny's fingers was poking straight out.

"I'll fix it later," Dr. Nicolletti said as he pulled and I pushed the gurney. It was difficult to move since one of the wheels had been bent in the accident.

We made it without further incident to the main road where the ambulance was waiting. Dr. Nicolletti thanked me for my assistance as we slid Lenny in and locked the gurney into place.

"So what do make of this?" I asked Dr. Nicolletti as he tossed his medical bag into the front seat.

"I'm not sure what killed him but I know what the coroner's report is going to say." He got into the car and turned on the ignition. He stared at me for a moment, then opened the window a crack and motioned for me to come closer. "I think your interpretation of the incident is not far from the truth. Quote me and I'll deny I said it."

I watched as he and Lenny drove off. Dr. Nicolletti had the lights flashing and the siren blaring. Although Lenny didn't need rush treatment, I figured the doctor didn't want to be alone with Lenny any longer than he had to be.

The whole incident was unnerving. I was just beginning to calm myself when I realized that something was missing—my dad. Normally he was right in the thick of things, or in the way of them.

"Dad," I shouted. No answer. I walked over to his car, thinking maybe he had decided to take a nap in the back seat. He wasn't there.

"Dad," I shouted, walking around in a circle. "DAD!"

I suppose it was the stress finally working its way to the surface, but all I could think was that my father, fed up with waiting, went looking for me, got lost, then hungry, pulled an apple off a tree, and now some apple tree was eating him. *Deep breath…deep breath,* I told myself.

I screamed for him again.

"Here I am," he said, grabbing my arm, nearly causing me to have a heart attack.

I turned around and glared at him. "Where have you been?" I asked him very slowly.

"I went exploring in the woods over there," he said, pointing in the direction of the Adam's abandoned farmhouse. "And you are not going to believe what I found…." A look of fascination mixed with horror was fixed upon his face.

"I don't want to know." I waved my hand and started to walk back to the car.

"But," he said following close behind me. "It's really spooky."

I stopped and turned to face him. I placed my index finger over my lips. "Don't say another word."

"But…."

"Not another word."

We got into the car and my father drove off. He didn't question me about Lenny, although I knew when he was finished pouting he would want to know every detail.

My dad parked the car and we quietly walked the Ghost Town Trail to the campsite.

"I'm sorry, Dad," I said, linking arms with him. "It's been a...." I paused to search for the right words. "A downright ghostly day for me."

"For me, too," he said softly. He took a deep breath and looked at me as if he were unsure whether I would hung him or bite him. He was still feeling a little dejected, I could tell.

We walked in silence for a few minutes when I suddenly realized where I got my talent for ghost-busting. "Dad, what's that saying about the acorn?"

"It doesn't' fall far from the tree," he answered, giving me a sidelong glance and what was either a smile or a grimace. I was hoping for the smile. "Let's not talk any more about oak trees."

"Okay. But there's a lot of truth in that saying, don't you think?"

"Darn right there is." My dad stopped walking and gave me a quick kiss on the forehead. "Everyone knows you got your good-looks from me."

"That's not what I meant."

"I know what you meant," he said, brushing a leaf off my shoulder. "Scary, isn't it?"

It sure was, I told him. What I didn't say was that it was scary in more ways than one.

The coroner's report was issued a few days after I returned to Pittsburgh. There was no mention of execution by plant life or screaming trees or killer ivy in Lenny's belly. The logger's death was listed as an accidental fall. I imagined what I would have added to the affidavit. This is an open and shut case of a tragic mishap. Nothing unusual. No paranormal activity. And especially, no interference by enchanted vegetation. Really, this fatality was practically humdrum. Honest. People crush themselves against tree branches surprisingly often."

Stan never told me to keep my mouth shut about the circumstances of Lenny's death. I'm sure he figured that no one would believe anything I had to say about it. After all, a ghost tale is just a ghost tale. And things that bump in the night are...?

(Madame Lorraine has been helping me to develop my own special skills, and very kindly turned this last story over to me for my response.)

Photograph by Frank Vennare/Studio V Productions

MS. CYNTHIA'S COMMENTS: *Keep in mind as we go through life, we travel together. Our feet touch the same earth, we share the same stars, we are warmed by the same sun. Each one of us holds a piece of truth, to be explored in a manner uniquely our own, then shared with one another. It is a truth that we hold sacred because it is sacred. Lenny, in this life, explored his truth and hopefully learned that we are not the masters of the world, but her stewards. Through his bizarre death he has passed a lesson on to us. If we are wise, we will heed the lesson: Take only what we need and leave the rest. (After discussing this case with the "ghost" crew, we decided to meet once a year for an annual tree planting party. You're all invited!)*

ENDING PRAYER

Oh, Lord,
when my time to go has come

The battle found
and death hath won

May the angels take my hand

And save me from
the shadowland

—A Polish Prayer

If you have any PSI experiences, such as ghost sightings, ESP (telepathy, clairvoyance, precognition or psychokinesis), contact with a departed spirit, psychic healing or any other paranormal event you wish to share contact us at:

The Ghost Crew
c/o Ceshore
440 Friday Road
Pittsburgh, PA 15209

For information regarding the paranormal:

American Society for Psychical Research, Inc.
5 West 73rd Street
New York, New York 10023
(212) 799-5050

European Journal of Parapsychology
Dept. of Psychology
University of Edinburgh
7 George Square
Edinburgh, EH8 9JZ
Scotland, G. B.
Phone: +44-131-650-3348

Exceptional Human Experience Network
414 Rockledge Road
New Bern, North Carolina 28562
(919) 636-8371

Global Intuition Network
(415) 256-1137

Journal of the Society for Psychical Research
The Society for Psychical Research
49 Marloes Road
London W8 6LA
England, G. B.

Journal of Scientific Exploration
ERL 306
Stanford University
Stanford, CA 94305-4055
(415) 593-8581

Parapsychological Association, Inc.
PO Box 797
Fairhaven, MA 02719

Parapsychology Foundation Counseling Bureau
(212) 628-1550

Rhine Research Center
Institute for Parapsychology
402 North Buchanan Boulevard
Durham, North Carolina 27701
(919) 688-8241

Spiritual Emergence Network
(408) 426-0902

On the Web:

Cognitive Sciences Laboratory
http://www.lfr.org

Consciousness Research Laboratory
http://www.PsiResearch.org

Franklin Pierce College
http://www.fpc.edu/edu/academic/behave/psych/para.htm

Koestler Parapsychology Unit
http://moebuis.psy.ed.ac.uk/kpu.html

Parapsychological Association
http://www.parapsych.org

Princeton Engineering Anomalies Research (PEAR)
http://www.parapsych.org

Rhine Research Center
http://www.rhine.org

University of Amsterdam Anomalous Cognition Project
http://info.psy.uva.nl./resedu/pn/anomal.html

SUGGESTED READING LIST:

Angel Answers by Ramer

Animal-Speak by Ted Andrews

Art of Dreaming by Mellick

Born to be Blessed by Judy McCoy Carman

ESP, Hauntings and Poltergeists by Loyd Auerbach

Heading Toward Omega: In Search of the Meaning of Near-Death Experiences by Kenneth Ring

Healing Words: The Power of Prayer, The Practice of Medicine by Larry Dossey, M.D.

Inner Counsel by Ann Nunley, Ph.D.

Introduction to Parapsychology by Harvey J. Irwin

Lucid Dreams in 30 Days: The Creative Sleep Program by Keith Harary & Patricia Weintraub

Out of Body Experiences: A Handbook by Janet Lee Mitchell

Parapsychology: The Controversy Science by Richard S. Broughton, Ph.D.

Quantum Healing by Deepak Chopra, M.D.

The Psychic Pathway by Sonia Choquette, Ph.D.

You are Psychic by Pete A. Sanders, Jr.

Vision of the Bereaved by Kay Witmer Woods

Author taking lessons from Madame Lorraine in contacting spirits.

At the cemetery Chelley discovers this statute inscribed only as Magdalene. The crew takes this coincidence as a sign from Maggie.

View of the cemetery.

The spot Maggie was laid to rest. (The light seen in the picture was not visible to us during the ceremony. It's probably just a reflection or something on the lens. Tricia believes it is Maggie entering sacred ground. We all hope so.)

Joe connecting with unknown spirit. Believed to be a new resident on the trail.

Joe taking samples of protoplasm to be analyzed on return to Pittsburgh.

Author and Joe walking section of trail which passes through Vintondale.

Red relaxing.

Red in trouble with his wife.

Red forgiven.

Chelley on the trail sketching.

Big Bear Cave

Gloria's crystal ball. Madame Lorraine plans to give this divining tool to a "gifted" student to honor the memory of her departed friend.

Maggie's ring that is owned by a distance relative who lives in the Twin Rocks area. To this day this tiny golden ring has never been worn by anyone other than Maggie.

Megan Davidson editing manuscript of Ghost Tales.

Tricia, author and Joe reviewing testimonies of strange phenomena that occurred on the Ghost Town Trail.

An early morning cup of coffee being enjoyed by the author before beginning another day of "ghosting."

Tricia, minus a tennis shoe, waving good-bye to her favorite ghost, SHOES.

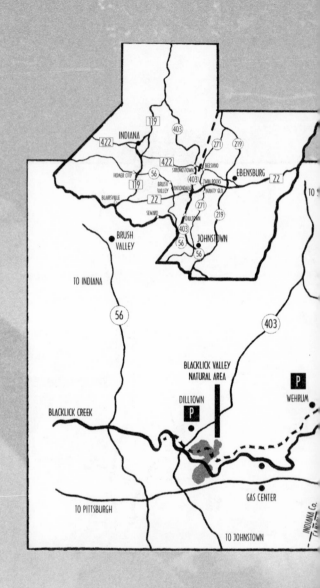

Map of the Ghost Town Trail.